D...

CONJUGATE
FUNCTIONS
FOR ENGINEERS

CONJUGATE FUNCTIONS
FOR ENGINEERS

A SIMPLE EXPOSITION OF THE SCHWARZ-CHRISTOFFEL TRANSFORMATION APPLIED TO THE SOLUTION OF PROBLEMS INVOLVING TWO-DIMENSIONAL FIELDS OF FORCE AND FLUX

By

MILES WALKER

M.A. (Cantab.), D.Sc. Eng. (Lond.), F.R.S.

*Sometime Professor of Electrical Engineering
in the Faculty of Technology in the
University of Manchester*

OXFORD UNIVERSITY PRESS
LONDON: HUMPHREY MILFORD
1933

OXFORD UNIVERSITY PRESS
AMEN HOUSE, E.C. 4
LONDON EDINBURGH GLASGOW
LEIPZIG NEW YORK TORONTO
MELBOURNE CAPETOWN BOMBAY
CALCUTTA MADRAS SHANGHAI
HUMPHREY MILFORD
PUBLISHER TO THE
UNIVERSITY

PRINTED IN GREAT BRITAIN AT THE UNIVERSITY PRESS, OXFORD
BY JOHN JOHNSON, PRINTER TO THE UNIVERSITY

PREFACE

CONJUGATE functions are not used by engineers as much as they might be. The subject is usually dealt with in the mathematical courses which form part of the training of our engineers at the Universities, but it is only seldom that a student takes to heart the instruction he receives and makes himself thoroughly familiar with the transformation of Schwarz and Christoffel. One reason for this is that the mathematician is often content with the rigid accuracy of his conceptions and does not see the advantage of making his abstract methods appeal to the type of engineer who understands things only by means of mental pictures and concrete models.

The author many years ago was introduced to the realities and to the unrealities of conjugate functions by that great teacher Henrici, whose enthusiasm was enough, one would think, to induce every member of his class to seize upon the subject as a most valuable tool. But only a few odd ones (not including the author) carried the method he taught into their practical work.

A few years ago the author had occasion to revive the subject and was greatly aided by Dr. J. Prescott and Mr. F. Bowman of the Manchester College of Technology. It then occurred to him that an elementary treatise dealing with the Schwarzian transformation from the point of view of the beginner might be of real service to those engineers who would like to make use of this powerful tool but have not the time to dig it out of their old mathematical notes. This little book therefore is essentially a beginner's book and can be read with ease by any one who has a knowledge of the elements of integral calculus and the algebra of complex quantities.

One of the difficulties that beset the beginner is to understand exactly what is meant when we say that a certain rectilinear figure is transformed into a straight horizontal line. It is hoped that the model suggested on p. 19 will be of as great use to the reader as it has been to the author in getting a clear picture of what is happening when figures are undergoing the transformation of Schwarz and Christoffel.

Sept. 1933   MILES WALKER

CONTENTS

CONJUGATE FUNCTIONS FOR ENGINEERS

THERE are many problems in physics and engineering in which we are concerned with a field of force such as a magnetic field, or a field of flow such as the flow of electric current or of a fluid. In some of these problems the lines of force or of flow are characterized by a certain simplicity of arrangement which makes the problems much simpler than they would be with a more complex arrangement. This simplicity exists in these cases because the lines are *continuous* throughout the whole region under consideration and *do not contain vortices.* Though tubes of force open out when extended to places where there is more room, they do not branch or form any loose ends. Lines do not begin or end within the region under consideration. This is expressed by saying that there is no *divergence.** The absence of vorticity is expressed by saying that *there is no curl.*

The imposing of these conditions on an electric or magnetic field implies such a simplification of the configuration of the equipotential surfaces and stream-lines of flux, *that, for a given disposition of its equipotential surfaces forming the boundaries* of the region under consideration, there can be only one pattern assumed by lines which are drawn to indicate the position of all the other equipotential surfaces and stream-lines. It is, therefore, possible in many cases where the boundary conditions are known, to find an expression for the values of V and F at any point throughout the region; the potential at each point being denoted by V and the flux vector by F.

Further, it sometimes happens that the distribution is two-dimensional in character, that is to say, it varies as we move in the plane of X, Y, but does not vary as we move in a direction Z at right angles to that plane. Thus the problem is still further simplified. This book only deals with such two-dimensional distributions, and aims at putting into simple words well-known methods of solving problems of this kind.

Here are a few of the kinds of field distribution that lend themselves to treatment by these methods.

* See footnote on p. 19.

(1) An electrostatic field between parallel cylindrical conductors of various shapes.

(2) An electric current in a uniform conducting sheet.

(3) A magnetic field between surfaces of ferromagnetic bodies; the surfaces being such as can be swept out by the movement of a figure (representing the configuration of the boundaries) at right angles to the plane of the figure. Such surfaces are, for instance, found on the armature and field-magnet of a dynamo when the armature is long as compared with the pole pitch. Here the 'figure' is a drawing of the iron parts of the dynamo looked at from one end of the shaft, and the surfaces in question are swept out by moving the figure parallel to the axis of the shaft.

(4) A magnetic field around a straight conductor carrying current in the neighbourhood of parallel ferromagnetic masses.

(5) The flow of heat in two dimensions through a homogeneous material which has arrived at a steady state.

(6) The stream-lines of fluid flowing in two dimensions through a homogeneous porous obstructing medium (not of course the microscopic stream-lines between the pores, but the stream-lines of the macrographic flow considered as a whole).

(7) The stream-lines of fluid flowing in two dimensions through an unobstructed channel provided that the lines of flow are continuous and free from rotational motion. This case is never met with in practice, but is an ideal case, useful for theoretical investigations.

Consider the simple case of an electric current flowing through a straight uniform strip of metal as shown in Fig. 1.

Let the strip be of such a material and such a thickness that it has a resistance of 1 ohm between opposite sides of a centimetre square as indicated in Fig. 2.

Then a current density of 1 ampere per cm. width of path will give a drop of 1 volt per cm. along that path. In order to fix our ideas we will suppose that the current flows from right to left. In Fig. 1 the stream-lines of the current are indicated by full lines, and the lines of equipotential by dotted lines. The value of the potential at any point is measured from some point taken arbitrarily as zero. For instance, in Fig. 1 the centre dotted line is taken arbitrarily as zero potential and then the values at the other lines are as indicated in the figure. Now let us consider another function called the 'stream function'.

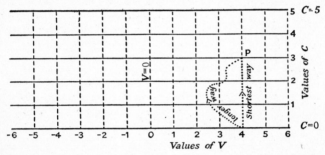

FIG. 1. Stream-lines of current in a uniform conducting strip having parallel sides. The equipotential lines are shown dotted.

The stream function is defined as follows: Imagine that we start on an itinerary from the base line $C = 0$ and cross the stream (of electric current) to the point P so that the direction of the current is everywhere at right angles to the itinerary. Then the value of the 'stream function' at the point P is the amount of current that we have crossed. If we go straight across the stream in Fig. 1, that will take us the shortest way from the base line to P because the stream-lines are horizontal in this case. If, on the other hand, we take a more circuitous route, the current will not be at right angles to our path; but the total current crossed will be the same for any given position of P. We must in this case add together all the little elements of current crossed, each element being $\mathbf{i}_a \times \cos\theta \times ds$ (see Fig. 3). Here $\mathbf{i}_a$ is a vector representing the current density,* ds is a little element of the path

FIG. 2. One square centimetre of thin conducting strip having a resistance of one ohm between opposite sides.

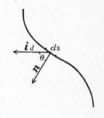

FIG. 3

* Current density here means amperes per cm. width of path taken at right angles to the flow. It is a vector quantity because it has direction as well as magnitude. Vector quantities in the text are denoted by heavy type.

traversed, and θ is the angle which a normal to the left of ds makes with $\mathbf{i}_d$. If we go past P and then come back to it the value of $\cos\theta$ on the way back becomes negative, so that however long and circuitous the path may be, the integral of all these elements will give the same value for the same point P. Thus the 'stream function' is a function that has a value which is definite for any given point and is independent of the itinerary by which the point is reached. It is a point function. Just as in the case of potential it is measured from an arbitrary zero. In Fig. 1 the line $C = 0$ is arbitrarily taken as zero.

This matter can be expressed in vector notation as follows: Let $\mathbf{i}_d$ be the current per cm. width of path (a vector) and $\mathbf{n}$ the unit normal to an element of path (the normal being taken to the left of the path) then the stream function is $\int \mathbf{i}_d \cdot \mathbf{n}\, ds$ where the dot indicates the scalar product of the vectors $\mathbf{i}_d$ and $\mathbf{n}$. Let θ be the angle between $\mathbf{i}_d$ and $\mathbf{n}$; then by definition $\mathbf{i}_d \cdot \mathbf{n} = i_d \cos\theta$ where i_d is the scalar value of $\mathbf{i}_d$. The stream function being the integral of a scalar quantity is of course scalar.

It will be noted that the electric force F at a point is equal to $i_d\rho$, where ρ is the resistance of 1 sq. cm. of strip (see Fig. 2), so that the potential $V = \int \rho\mathbf{i}_d \cdot d\mathbf{s}$. Here $d\mathbf{s}$ is a little vector along the path. If we take $\rho = 1$ ohm, as in this case, V is the line integral of the current density taken *along* the path of the current and C is the line integral of the current taken *across* the path.

The equipotential lines are necessarily at right angles to the stream-lines that cross them because the electric force F at every point is the space-gradient of V and the current flows in the direction of the electric force.

Consider now the case where an electric current, flowing in an infinite uniform sheet of resisting material, is taken out at a point or sink S and fed in at an infinite distance from the sink. The lines of flow are radial, as indicated by the full lines in Fig. 4, and the equipotential lines are circles, as indicated by the dotted lines. Let the total current of I amperes be flowing in the sheet. Then the current density i_d, at any radius r, is $I/2\pi r$ and the electric force $F = I\rho/2\pi r$. The difference of electric potential between any two points at radius r_1 and r_2 respectively is

$$V_{r_2} - V_{r_1} = \frac{I\rho}{2\pi} \int_{r_1}^{r_2} \frac{1}{r}\, dr = \frac{I\rho}{2\pi} \log\frac{r_2}{r_1} + \text{const.}$$

The numbers attached to equipotential circles in Fig. 4 are therefore proportional to the logarithms of the radii of the circles. For simplicity we will make the resistance of a sq. cm. of the sheet equal to 1 ohm ($\rho = 1$). If we arbitrarily mark $V = 0$ at the circle of radius 1 cm. we eliminate the constant of integration in the general integral $\int 1/r\, dr$ because log 1 $= 0$. It is convenient

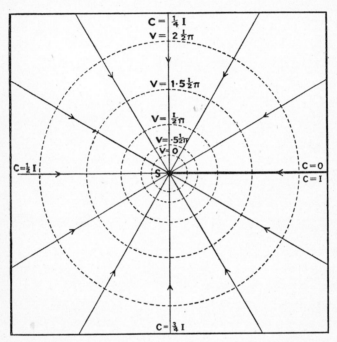

FIG. 4. Stream-lines of current flowing to a sink S from a distant boundary. The equipotential lines are shown by the dotted circles.

for many purposes to take this circle of unit radius as at zero potential, but if in any particular problem that circle is at some other potential (measured from another point taken arbitrarily as zero) the constant of integration must be adjusted accordingly. In attaching values to the radial lines for the stream function we may arbitrarily mark any line $C = 0$. The value of the stream function for any other line is the current crossed in getting to that line from the zero line. Taking arbitrarily the horizontal line drawn from S to the right as zero, the values of the stream function are as shown in Fig. 4, provided we reach each line shown by starting from the zero line and passing round the sink S in a counter-clockwise direction. Here the normal to the itinerary is taken to the left as in Fig. 1. If, however, we proceed to any line by going clockwise around the sink, then the numbers to be attached to the lines would be as indicated in Fig. 5. It will be seen that the values in Fig. 5 differ from those in Fig. 4 by the

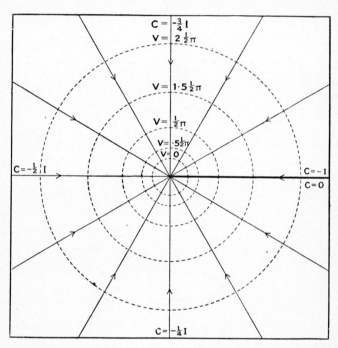

FIG. 5. Showing how the values of the stream function at various lines differ from the values given in Fig. 4 when the itinerary goes clockwise around the sink instead of counter-clockwise.

constant I. In fact, an indefinite number of values could be given to each line, differing by mI where m is a whole number, because every time we pass around the sink we cross I amperes, and starting from any line we could reach it again after going m times around the sink S.

In order that we may have only one value for the current function at any radial line it is convenient to draw a radial barrier shown by the thick line in Fig. 4 and to limit our movement in the region under consideration so that we never cross the barrier.

Under these conditions the radial lines of Fig. 4 have the values marked upon them and each radial line has only one value, namely, the total current crossed in passing in the counter-clockwise direction from the zero line to the line in question.

The same convention may be adopted when ascribing values to the magnetic potential at any point outside a conductor

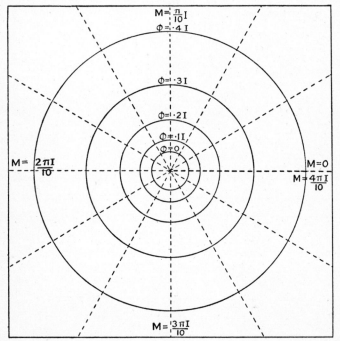

FIG. 6. The radial lines of equi-magnetic potential (shown dotted) in the vicinity of a straight conductor carrying a current I at right angles to the paper. The traces on the paper of the cylinders of constant flux are shown by the circles.

carrying current. In Fig. 6 we are supposed to have a conductor at right angles to the paper carrying a current I amperes flowing away from the observer. In this case the surfaces of equi-magnetic potential are radial planes at right angles to the paper and the surfaces of constant stream function or constant flux are cylinders concentric with the conductor. If we pass from circle $\phi = 0$ to a point anywhere on the circle $0 \cdot 3I$ the line integral of the flux density crossed is equal to $0 \cdot 3I$. The concentric circles in Fig. 6 are the traces of the vertical concentric cylinders

on the plane of the paper. Consider a cylinder $0.3I$ standing
1 cm. high from the paper. It encloses a flux $0.3I$ between
itself and the cylinder $\phi = 0$. This case is the inverse of the case
considered in Fig. 4. The equipotential lines are radial and the
equiflux lines circles. Let us arbitrarily draw a barrier from the
conductor horizontally to the right. Let points immediately above
the barrier have ascribed to them zero magnetic potential and
be marked $M = 0$. Then going around the conductor counter-
clockwise against the direction of the magnetic field we arrive at
the underside of the barrier, having made one turn. The magnetic
potential of the points immediately below the barrier have a value
$M = 4\pi I/10$. When we have travelled through only 90°, the value
of $M = \pi I/10$; after 180°, $2\pi I/10$; and so on. If it were not for
the barrier and the decision not to cross it, the potential of any point
would not be clearly ascertained, because it would depend upon
the way we had travelled to it from the surface where $M = 0$.
The spacing of the surfaces of constant stream function is the
same as the spacing of the equipotential lines in Fig. 4. That is
to say, the numbers attached to the circles are proportional to
the logarithms of the radii. It is convenient to mark the cylinder of unit radius $\phi = 0$ because $\log 1 = 0$. This eliminates
the arbitrary constant referred to on p. 4. On this basis the
marking of the other cylinders is obtained from the formula
$\phi = 0.2I \log r$. Here we are integrating the flux in a cylinder
1 cm. deep from the paper. For the same reason as in Fig. 1 the
equipotential lines in Figs. 4 and 6 are at right angles to the lines
of constant stream function. The lines are, of course, the traces
on the plane of the paper of two systems of surfaces which cut
each other at right angles.

These orthogonal systems of lines and surfaces are analogous
to the orthogonal systems that arise from the plotting of certain
functions of a complex variable known as conjugate functions.
For this reason amongst others, the study of conjugate functions
is of especial interest to the physicist and engineer.

The complex variable will first be considered in connexion
with the simple rectangular distribution shown in Fig. 1 and
afterwards in connexion with more complicated distributions.

It is convenient to express the position of any point P in Fig. 1 (which for the purpose of discussion may be regarded as P in Fig. 7) in the notation commonly employed to indicate the position of a point in the plane of complex numbers.* The position of P is given by the two coordinates x and y. The symbol jy indicates

---

* The reader is supposed to be familiar with complex algebra and the plane of numbers. For the benefit of those who are a little rusty on this subject we append the following note: All real numbers are represented by the positions of points on the horizontal axis of x in Fig. 7. The figure is supposed to be drawn to some agreed scale, say 1 cm. = one unit. Whole numbers are at the points 1, 2, 3, etc., and fractional numbers are at points in between. Positive numbers are measured off to the right of the origin O and negative numbers to the left. Multiplying a number by j (or the square root of -1) has the effect of turning the horizontal line representing that number through an angle of 90° so as to make it vertical. Multiplying by j again turns it through another right angle; so that multiplying by j^2 (or -1) has the effect of making a positive number negative. A complex number consists of two parts, a real part, say 4 (in Fig. 7), and an unreal or imaginary part, say $j3$ (in Fig. 7). Every complex number is represented by some point in the plane of numbers just as P represents $4+j3$ in Fig. 7. Now by De Moivre's theorem

$$m\epsilon^{j\theta} = m\cos\theta + jm\sin\theta.$$

The point P in Fig. 7 can be written $5\epsilon^{j\theta}$, where $\theta =$ the angle whose tangent is $\frac{3}{4}$, or it may be written

$$5\cos\theta + j5\sin\theta = 4+j3.$$

The coefficient m is called the modulus of the number and the angle θ the 'argument' (a very confusing name).

To raise any complex number to any power we raise the modulus to the power in question and multiply the argument by the index of the power.

Thus

$$(m\epsilon^{j\theta})^2 = m^2\epsilon^{j2\theta}.$$

This is easily carried out graphically. Thus, taking the value of z from Fig. 7, $z^2 = 25\epsilon^{j2\theta}$, and would be represented by a line 25 cm. long, making an angle 2θ with the horizontal.

Fractional powers are found in the same way,

$$\sqrt{z} = z^{\frac{1}{2}} = \sqrt{m}\epsilon^{j\theta/2}.$$

The square root of the complex number represented by P in Fig. 7 gives us a line 2·235 units long, making an angle $\theta/2$ with the axis of x. Any function of a complex number consists of a real part and an imaginary part. Instances will be found on pp. 10 and 12. In general, the real part is a function of both x and y, and the unreal part is also a function of x and y. It is the interesting relations between these quantities that have given rise to the study of conjugate functions.

In any equation between complex numbers we can always equate the real part on one side of the equation to the real part on the other side, and do the same with the imaginary parts.

that y units of length are measured vertically, so that $x+jy$ gives the hypotenuse of the right-angled triangle in Fig. 7. For shortness we write $x+jy = z$,† and though from one point of view z is a vector giving the position of P with regard to the origin, we deal with it as a complex number and can take any function of it, algebraic, trigonometrical, or hyperbolic. For instance in Fig. 7, $z = 4+j3$. The 4 is measured horizontally and the 3 vertically. In the simple case supposed in Fig. 1 where the current density $= 1$ we can at once find the value of the potential and stream function at any point from the value of z, for

$$V+jC = x+jy = z. \tag{1}$$

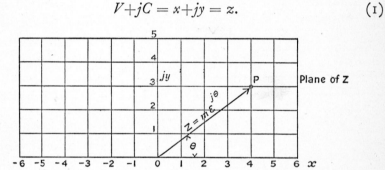

FIG. 7. Showing how the position of a point P (such as that in Fig. 1) can be expressed as $x+jy$ or as $m\epsilon^{j\theta}$.

Taking the values of P from Fig. 1 and Fig. 7, $V+jC = 4+j3$. Therefore, equating real terms we get $V = 4$, and equating unreal terms we get $C = 3$. In a case where $\rho = 1$ but the current density i_a is not equal to unity we have

$$V+jC = i_a(x+jy) = i_a z. \tag{2}$$

Thus if the current density had been 10 amperes per cm. width of path, then we should have

$$V+jC = 10(x+jy) = 10z,$$

or $\qquad\qquad V = 10x \quad \text{and} \quad C = 10y;$

all the values in Fig. 1 would be simply multiplied by 10.

This is an instance of the potential and stream functions being very simple functions of z. Now let us consider some more

† It should be noted that this use of the letter z as a shorthand sign for $x+jy$ is entirely different from the use of Z for an axis at right angles to X and Y.

complicated functions of z. What kind of distribution of V and C should we expect from the equation

$$V+jC = \epsilon^{j\pi/6}z\,?$$

We can give the position of any point in polar coordinates m, θ. We have $z = x+jy = m\epsilon^{j\theta}$, where $m = \sqrt{x^2+y^2}$ and $\theta = \tan^{-1}(y/x)$. Therefore

$$V+jC = m\epsilon^{j(\theta+\frac{1}{6}\pi)}. \tag{3}$$

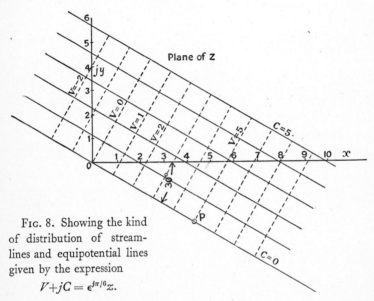

Plane of Z

FIG. 8. Showing the kind of distribution of stream-lines and equipotential lines given by the expression
$$V+jC = \epsilon^{j\pi/6}z.$$

The angle of $\pi/6$ radians $= 30°$. If we tilt the parallel lines in Fig. 1 through $30°$ with the hands of a clock, we get the distribution of stream-lines expressed by equation (3). To check this, take any point, say P (Fig. 8), where $z = 5\epsilon^{-j\pi/6}$. Here $m = 5$ and $\theta = -\pi/6$. $\therefore m\epsilon^{j(\theta+\frac{1}{6}\pi)} = m\epsilon^0 = m = 5+j\text{o} = V+jC$. By equating real and unreal terms we get $V = 5$ and $C = \text{o}$. These are the values at P in the distribution shown in Fig. 8.

On p. 12 other functions of z are considered, z^2 on p. 16, and $\cosh cz$ on p. 48.

The fact that the equipotential lines always cut the stream-lines at right angles makes it convenient to use these functions of z to express the distribution of the field. Every function of a complex quantity consists of a real part, say ϕ, and an unreal part, say $j\psi$, so that we may write

$$f(z) = f(x+jy) = \phi + j\psi.$$

As a rule ϕ is some function of both x and y, and ψ is some other function of x and y.

Thus, if
$$f(z) = z^2 = (x+jy)^2,$$
$$\phi + j\psi = x^2 - y^2 + j\, 2xy,$$

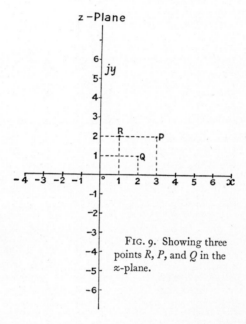

z –Plane

FIG. 9. Showing three points R, P, and Q in the z-plane.

so that the real part $\phi = x^2 - y^2$, and the coefficient of j, namely $\psi = 2xy$ (see p. 7 and Fig. 13).

Again let $f(z) = \log z = \log(m\epsilon^{j\theta}) = \log m + j\theta$,

$$\therefore \; \phi = \log m \quad \text{and} \quad \psi = \theta.$$

At this stage it is a good plan for the beginner to plot several functions of a complex variable and to note the variation which occurs in $f(z)$ or $f(x+jy)$ when a small change is made in x and compare it with the variation when a small change is made in y. Good examples to take are kz, z^2, $\log z$, $\cosh cz$.

The study of the case where

$$f(z) = z^2 = w = \phi + j\psi \tag{4}$$

is illustrated in Figs. 9 and 10. Fig. 9 is simply the plane of z. The point P represents $z = 3+j2$. In Fig. 10 the values of ϕ are taken as abscissae and the values of ψ as ordinates. We may for convenience call this the plane of w. As

$$z^2 = (x+jy)^2 = x^2 - y^2 + j\,2xy = \phi + j\psi,$$

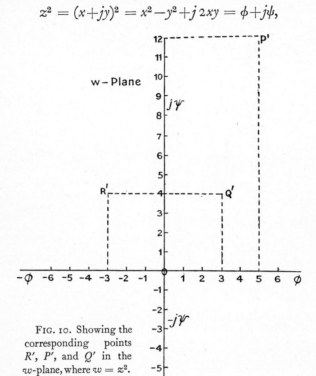

FIG. 10. Showing the corresponding points R', P', and Q' in the w-plane, where $w = z^2$.

we have $\phi = x^2 - y^2$ and $\psi = 2xy$. For every point in the z-plane (Fig. 9) there is a corresponding point in the w-plane (Fig. 10). Thus, taking the point $3+j2$ we have $\phi = 3^2 - 2^2 = 5$ and $\psi = 2 \times 3 \times 2 = 12$, so the point P' with coordinates $(5, 12)$ in the w-plane corresponds to the point P with coordinates $(3, 2)$ in the z-plane. The point Q' with coordinates $(3, 4)$ in the w-plane corresponds to the point Q with coordinates $(2, 1)$ in the z-plane. Where y is greater than x the value of ϕ will be negative. Thus for the point $R = (1, 2)$ we get the point $R' = (-3, 4)$ in the w-plane.

Let us now confine our attention to points in the z-plane that are very near to the point P. They will correspond to points that are very near P' in the w-plane. By taking a number of values of x and y very nearly equal to the coordinates 3 and 2 we could get a number of points very close to P' and for a definite little change in z, say dz, taken in any direction whatever, we get a definite little change in w, say dw. For the kind of functions here dealt with, if the length dz is constant, whatever its direction, the length dw is constant. When the direction of dz is changed, the value of dy/dx is changed. For the functions under discussion the value of the ratio dw/dz at any point is independent of the value of dy/dx. That is to say, it is independent of the direction in which the change in z is made. In the particular case taken the function $z^2 = (x+jy)^2$ is of such a nature that

$$\frac{\partial \phi}{\partial x} = \frac{\partial \psi}{\partial y} \quad \text{and} \quad \frac{\partial \phi}{\partial y} = -\frac{\partial \psi}{\partial x}. \tag{5}$$

Since $\qquad \phi = x^2 - y^2; \ \psi = 2xy,$

$$\frac{\partial \phi}{\partial x} = 2x \quad \text{and} \quad \frac{\partial \psi}{\partial y} = 2x, \ \text{the sign being the same.}$$

Further $\qquad \dfrac{\partial \phi}{\partial y} = -2y \quad \text{and} \quad \dfrac{\partial \psi}{\partial x} = 2y, \ \text{the sign being opposite.}$

When the relation (5) holds, the value of dw/dz is independent of the direction in which dz is taken in the z-plane. The proof of this is as follows:

$$\frac{dw}{dz} = \frac{d\phi + j d\psi}{dx + j dy} = \frac{\dfrac{\partial \phi}{\partial x} dx + j \dfrac{\partial \psi}{\partial x} dx + \dfrac{\partial \phi}{\partial y} dy + j \dfrac{\partial \psi}{\partial y} dy}{dx + j dy}.$$

Divide top and bottom by dx:

$$\frac{dw}{dz} = \frac{\dfrac{\partial \phi}{\partial x} + j \dfrac{\partial \psi}{\partial x} + \left(\dfrac{\partial \phi}{\partial y} + j \dfrac{\partial \psi}{\partial y} \right) \dfrac{dy}{dx}}{1 + j \dfrac{dy}{dx}}.$$

Write this in the form

$$\frac{dw}{dz} = \frac{a + b \dfrac{dy}{dx}}{1 + j \dfrac{dy}{dx}},$$

where $\qquad a=\left(\dfrac{\partial \phi}{\partial x}+j\dfrac{\partial \psi}{\partial x}\right)$ and $b=\left(\dfrac{\partial \phi}{\partial y}+j\dfrac{\partial \psi}{\partial y}\right).$

Now the value of this expression is not independent of the value of dy/dx unless there exists the relation $ja = b$. For those functions of z where this relation holds we can write

$$\frac{dw}{dz}=\frac{a\left(1+j\dfrac{dy}{dx}\right)}{1+j\dfrac{dy}{dx}}=a.$$

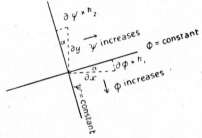

FIG. 11. Illustrating how $\dfrac{\partial \phi}{\partial x}=\dfrac{\partial \psi}{\partial y}$.

That is to say, where $\qquad ja=b,$

or $\qquad j\left(\dfrac{\partial \phi}{\partial x}+j\dfrac{\partial \psi}{\partial x}\right)=\dfrac{\partial \phi}{\partial y}+j\dfrac{\partial \psi}{\partial y},$

or $\qquad j\dfrac{\partial \phi}{\partial x}-\dfrac{\partial \psi}{\partial x}=\dfrac{\partial \phi}{\partial y}+j\dfrac{\partial \psi}{\partial y},$

or $\qquad \dfrac{\partial \phi}{\partial x}=\dfrac{\partial \psi}{\partial y}$ and $\dfrac{\partial \phi}{\partial y}=-\dfrac{\partial \psi}{\partial x},$ $\qquad (5)$

the value of dw/dz is independent of the value of dy/dx; that is, it is independent of the slope of dz. Such functions of z as make this true are called 'analytic' functions. Each has a real part ϕ and an unreal part $j\psi$, where ϕ and ψ are functions of x and y such that the above relation (5) holds. ϕ and ψ are then called *conjugate functions.*

The effect of equation (5) can be seen from Figs. 11 and 12. The thick black lines $\phi =$ constant and $\psi =$ constant cut one another at right angles. If we go a little way from the intersection along ∂x, we get to a point where ϕ is greater and the little perpendicular to the ϕ line is $\partial \phi \times k_1$. Similarly, if we go the same distance in a vertical direction along ∂y, we come to a point where ψ is a little greater and the perpendicular upon the ψ line is marked $\partial \psi \times k_2$. Now the statement that

$$\frac{\partial \phi}{\partial x} = \frac{\partial \psi}{\partial y}$$

means that not only are the black lines at right angles; but the rate of change of ϕ and ψ in directions at right angles to their black lines are the same, that is, that $k_1 = k_2$.

If now we drop perpendiculars from the ends of ∂x and ∂y on to the ψ and ϕ lines respectively as in Fig. 12 we see that while $\partial \psi$ is still positive, $\partial \phi$ is negative. This accounts for the negative sign in the equation. Analytic functions with which we are concerned here are such as make the above relations hold.

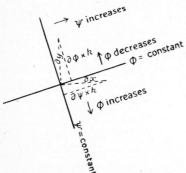

FIG. 12. Illustrating how $\dfrac{\partial \phi}{\partial y} = -\dfrac{\partial \psi}{\partial x}$.

In the expression

$$w = f(x+jy) = \phi + j\psi,$$

both ϕ and ψ are functions of x and y. Thus we may write $\phi = f_\phi(x,y)$ and $\psi = f_\psi(x,y)$. Then if we give ϕ a constant value, say ϕ_1, the expression

$$f_\phi(x, y) = \phi_1$$

(a constant) is the equation to a line in the z-plane. For instance, let $w = z^2 = (x+jy)^2 = x^2 - y^2 + j\,2xy$. The real part

$$\phi = f_\phi(x,y) = x^2 - y^2$$

and the imaginary part $\psi = f_\psi(x,y) = 2xy$. Take for ϕ_1 the value 1. We then have the equation $x^2 - y^2 = 1$. Giving x various values and finding the corresponding values of y we can plot the dotted curve in Fig. 13 marked $\phi = 1$. It is a hyperbola asymptotic to the straight line $\phi = 0$. $\phi = 2$ gives us another curve.

Now consider $\psi = f_\psi(x, y)$ and take constant values for ψ. For instance, let $\psi = 2xy$, and take for ψ the value 1. Then

$$2xy = 1.$$

This gives us the full line curve $\psi = 1$. It is a hyperbola asymptotic to the axes of x and y.

Now it will be seen that the full line curves cut the dotted curves at right angles. We have two systems of curves orthogonal to one another giving values at every point to the conjugate functions ϕ and ψ.

Suppose we have a large uniform sheet as in Fig. 13 of resisting

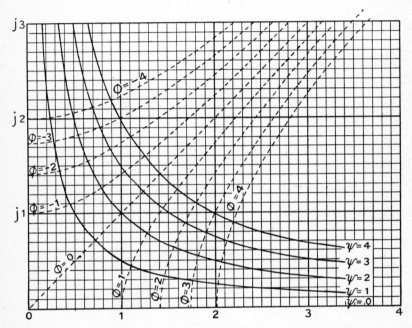

FIG. 13. Showing how the curves plotted (in the plane of z) for constant values of the conjugate functions, ϕ and ψ, cut one another at right angles.

material with one corner at O and two edges along the axes of x and y. An electric current fed into the sheet at the line $\phi = 4$ and out of the sheet at $\phi = -4$ would have its stream-lines along the full ψ lines, and the lines of equipotential would be along the dotted lines. This is proved on p. 33.

Referring now to Fig. 10 in which the values of ϕ and ψ were set out as rectangular coordinates, we see that the lines $\phi = 1, 2,$ 3, etc., and $\psi = 1, 2, 3,$ etc., are straight lines. A parallel distribution of equipotential and stream function lines is indicated by the expression

$$V + jC = k(\phi + j\psi) = kw,$$

where k is a constant.

Now let the connexion between the w-plane and the z-plane be given by the equation $w = z^2$ as in Fig. 13, and we see that the straight lines corresponding to constant values of ϕ and ψ in the w-plane are converted in the z-plane to hyperbolae that give ϕ and ψ equal to the same constant values respectively. Or we may take it the other way. Let the z-plane have the distribution shown in Fig. 13 in which $\phi = x^2 - y^2$ and $\psi = 2xy$. The effect of squaring z (that is, the effect of $w = z^2$) is to straighten out all the hyperbolae in the z-plane to straight lines in the w-plane. That is to say, the transferring of the curves $\phi = $ constant and $\psi = $ constant (corresponding to $w = z^2$) from the z-plane of Fig. 13 to the w-plane of Fig. 10 opens out all the hyperbolae in the former to straight lines in the latter.

But suppose now that the current in the w-plane followed a more complicated law, say $V + jC = F(w) = F_V(\phi, \psi) + F_C(\phi, \psi)$.

There would be everywhere throughout the w-plane two systems of curves, equipotential $F_V(\phi, \psi) = $ constant, and stream-line $F_C(\phi, \psi) = $ constant, cutting each other at right angles; and as every point P' in the w-plane has its corresponding point P in the z-plane there would be everywhere in the z-plane another two systems of curves $V = $ constant and $C = $ constant, whose shape might depend on more or less complicated functions of z.

A concrete example will make this clear. Consider first the expression $V + jC = \log w$ in conjunction with Fig. 4. Take the origin of w at the sink S and express w in polar coordinates $w = m' \epsilon^{j\theta'}$, where m' is the distance of the point P' from the origin. Then $\log w = \log m' + j\theta'$. The real part of the expression $\log m'$ gives us V and the unreal $j\theta'$ gives us jC. We have already considered on p. 4 the kind of current distribution such that the potential V is proportional to the logarithm of the radius m and such that the current function C is proportional to the angle θ'. Thus a distribution of the potential and current functions such as shown in Fig. 4 can be expressed by saying that $V + jC = \log w$.

Now let $w = z^2$.

$$V + jC = \log z^2 = 2 \log z = 2 \log(m\epsilon^{j\theta})$$
$$= 2 \log m + j\, 2\theta.$$

Here m is the distance of the point P from the origin in the z-plane. The kind of distribution obtained in the z-plane is similar to that in the w-plane but the current density is twice as great and the equipotential circles are nearer together. V is equal to $\log m'$ in the w-plane, and equal to $2 \log m$ in the z-plane. The stream-lines are still radial but have their values doubled. A current converging to a point S and spread out over the whole angle 2π in the w-plane is crowded into the space above the axis of x in the z-plane and is spread out only over the angle π.

Where $V + jC$ is a more complicated function of w the equations for the equipotential lines and stream-lines may be still more complicated functions of z.

The burden of this book is to follow how patterns of equipotential lines and stream-lines drawn in the w-plane are changed in form when transformed to the z-plane when there is some known relation between w and z.

As stated on p. 1 the kinds of field with which we are concerned are such that there is no divergence* and no curl.

In visualizing the meaning of some of the expressions which are given later in this book the student will be assisted if he can look upon space occupied by a field, having the properties described on p. 1, as being filled with a substance having the structure described in the next paragraph.

Imagine a substance resembling rubber sponge or soap-suds in which the vesicles are infinitely small. Assume further that, while remaining spherical in shape, the vesicles are infinitely

---

* For the benefit of the reader who is familiar with vector analysis, the above-mentioned characteristics of the lines are more completely expressed as follows:

Let there be a definite potential at every point and let this be denoted by V. Then the space-gradient of V or ∇V (grad V) gives the force F at any point. If there is no divergence $\nabla \cdot F = 0$ or $\nabla \cdot \nabla V = \nabla^2 V = 0$. Further, we have assumed that every point has a definite potential. It can be shown that, where this is so, the curl of $F = 0$, or $\nabla_\wedge F = 0$. Taking F as a vector representing the stream-line in the flow of a liquid, when $\nabla_\wedge F = 0$ there is no vorticity.

compressible and infinitely expansible. If, for instance, a portion of the substance fills a hollow sphere, the size of the sphere can be made smaller and smaller without limit, compressing the substance, or made bigger and bigger without limit, the sponge expanding and always touching the inner walls of the sphere. Imagine further that the sponge is sufficiently solid in structure to retain in position any pattern that may be drawn throughout its substance by means of equipotential surfaces or stream-lines. An alteration of pattern will, of course, occur when the external shape of the sponge is changed, but not otherwise. It is convenient to imagine this sponge in contact with external solid

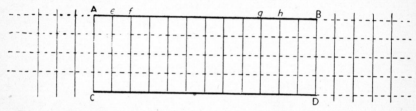

FIG. 14. Stream-lines and equipotential lines supposed to be drawn on the hypothetical spongy substance filling the space between the two solid plates *AB* and *CD*.

surfaces, by the movement of which the substance can be deformed. But while the external surface of the sponge always touches the solid surface it is not attached to it in any way that will prevent relative motion in a direction tangential to the plane of the surface. The sponge can everywhere slide along the bounding surface but can never leave it. Having defined the nature of the sponge and its quasi attachment to the boundary surfaces, let us consider how the patterns of the equipotential lines and stream-lines will alter as the sponge is deformed by the movement of the solid surfaces.

First imagine the sponge placed between two long, flat, parallel plates as in Fig. 14.

In practice one could not get the plates infinitely large, so that there would be free surfaces which would interfere with the theoretical behaviour of this sponge supposed to be placed between infinite plates. But we can imagine that everything goes on without this interference, and that we are able to draw, on the free surface next to us, equipotentials shown as dotted lines in Fig. 14, and the stream-lines shown as full lines. The pattern is like that in Fig. 1, except that the stream-lines are vertical. The distance between two full lines *e* and *f* near *A* and *C* is the same as the distance between *g* and *h* at the other end of the figure.

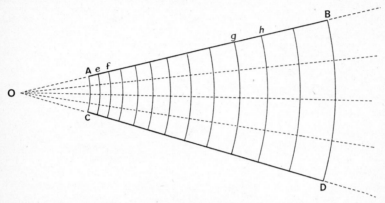

FIG. 15. Showing how the stream-lines and equipotential lines change shape when the plates *AB* and *CD* are inclined to one another.

Now let *A* and *C* be brought nearer together and *B* and *D* separated as in Fig. 15. The dotted lines will now converge towards *A* and *C*. The spherical vesicles will be compressed between *A* and *C* and, as they are supposed to remain spherical, the full lines *ef* will be closer together in the same ratio as the dotted lines near them. In the little sector *OAC* we can imagine that we have compressed all the squares that extend from the line *AC* to *O* in Fig. 15. As there is infinite vertical compression we get an

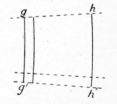

FIG. 16. Showing how in its finest texture the con-figuration of Fig. 15 is made up of squares.

infinite number of squares compressed into a finite sector. The full lines *g* and *h* are opened out in the same ratio as the dotted lines at that part. The full lines are circles having a centre at *O* and cut the radial stream-lines everywhere at right angles. Let us take one of the distorted squares lying between the lines *g* and *h* in Fig. 15 and magnify it as shown at *g*, *h*, *h'*, *g'*, in Fig. 16.

We can now draw in some intermediate equipotential lines and stream-lines as shown in the corner. These new dotted lines are more nearly parallel than *gh* and *g'h'* and the parts of the circles bounding the little square are more nearly straight than *gg'* and *hh'*. We see that if we were to magnify this little square and draw stream-lines and equipotential lines nearer together, we should get a figure which would approximate to a square as nearly as we like. This is always true however much distortion we get of the main body of the sponge, the pattern in its finest texture is made up of an infinite number of squares that depart from perfect squareness by an infinitely small amount. This must be

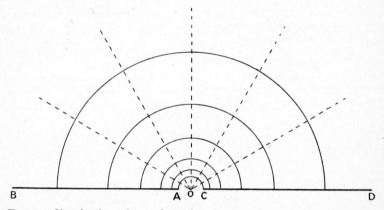

FIG. 17. Showing how the configuration changes when the plates are opened out so as to be in the same straight line *BAOCD*.

true where the two systems of lines cut each other at right angles.

Let us now open out the surfaces *AB* and *CD* until they lie in the same straight line, as shown in Fig. 17. The surfaces are supposed to extend to infinity beyond *B* and *D*. The sponge vesicles or soap-suds foam up to infinity beyond and above *B* and *D*, and are supposed to be infinitely compressed towards the point *O*. The stream-line *AC* is now a semicircle, as are all the stream-lines. It will be seen that a pattern like that given in Fig. 14 has been distorted into a pattern like that in Fig. 17 by the movement of two equipotential planes.

Imagine now *any* pattern drawn on our sponge with equipotential lines and stream-lines complying with the conditions laid down on pp. 15 and 19, and fit two solid surfaces to two equipotential surfaces. The patterns could, of course, be expressed as functions of z. Any movement of the solid surfaces will lead to a new pattern and change the functions of z. For any given configuration of the surfaces there is only one pattern that satisfies the conditions, and that one is the solution of the Laplacian equation for that configuration of the boundary. If we could only get a spongy substance of the right kind and make it behave as described on p. 20 one method of solving the Laplacian equation for a given complicated configuration of the equipotential surfaces would be as follows: First of all straighten out the solid surfaces (which represent the given equipotential surfaces) until they make some simple configuration, say of two long straight lines (as in Fig. 17) to which we can easily fit a pattern of orthogonal lines. Then draw the simple pattern that would be taken by the orthogonal lines. Now fold the surfaces back to the configuration required in the problem, and the pattern will assume a new shape which gives the solution we want.

While we cannot find a substance of the right kind to do this, we can find a mathematical process which in effect does the same thing. It gives us the change that occurs in the expressions for the equipotential lines and stream-lines when the boundary of the figure is distorted. This leads us to the theorem due to Schwarz[*] and Christoffel.[†] The theorem gives us a differential equation which embodies the nature of the change in a function of z bounded by any straight-sided figure in order that the boundary may be opened out into one straight line; the opening-out involving, of course, the distortion of the function. For example, the function $k(x+jy)$ in Fig. 14 in the z-plane was distorted to $(k/\pi)\log r + j(k/\pi)\theta$ in Fig. 17 by the opening out of the parallel lines AB and CD into one straight horizontal line $BACD$. The differential equation in question embodies the nature of the change of the function $k(x+jy)$ when the said distortion occurs.

Let us take any rectilinear figure $ABCD$ in the z-plane as in Fig. 18. We are concerned only with points such as $P = m\epsilon^{j\theta}$ which

---

[*] 'Ueber einige Abbildungsaufgaben', *Crelle*, 70 (1869), p. 105.

[†] 'Sul problema delle temperature stazionarie,' *Annali de Matematica*, 1 (1867), p. 89. See also *Recent Researches in Electricity and Magnetism* by J. J. Thomson (1893), p. 208.

lie within the figure or in the boundary. We are not concerned with points outside the figure. Consider another plane called the *t*-plane in which the axes are ξ and $j\eta$ (Fig. 19). In this plane we are only concerned with points such as P' which lie above the horizontal axis. The axis of ξ goes to $-\infty$ on the left and to $+\infty$ on the right, while $j\eta$ goes from o to $+\infty$ in the vertical direction. Let the figure $ABCD$ be filled with our hypothetical

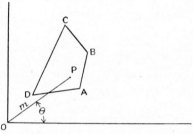

FIG. 18. The plane of z containing a rectilinear figure $ABCD$ which forms the boundaries of a field of stream-lines and equipotential lines.

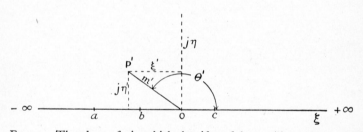

FIG. 19. The plane of t in which the sides of the rectilinear figure $ABCD$ have been opened out along the straight line $-\infty aboc + \infty$.

sponge upon which is drawn any orthogonal systems of lines satisfying the conditions laid out on p. 15. Cut into the figure at any point, say D, and imagine the line DA laid along the axis of ξ in the *t*-plane and stretched from $-\infty$ to a point a, whose position in the axis of ξ is for the moment not ascertained. Let the line AB also be laid along ξ stretching between the points a and b, the length ab being as yet unknown. Let the line BC be laid along ξ, stretching between the assumed points bc, and then let CD be stretched along ξ from c to $+\infty$. It should be explained that the point a is supposed to be a units of distance, say a centimetres from the origin O in the *t*-plane. There is no obvious connexion between the lengths a, b, c, etc., and the lengths of AB, CD, etc. Whatever relations do exist can be ascertained during the solution of the problem, as will appear later.

While the straightening-out process of the boundary is proceeding, the spongy substance within the boundary is supposed to escape and foam upwards and to left and right, filling a semicircular region of infinite radius above the axis of ξ in the t-plane.

On account of the properties (see p. 20) ascribed to the spongy substance, the orthogonal systems of lines drawn upon it still remain orthogonal systems, although the pattern will be of a quite different shape after the figure $ABCD$ has been opened out. If now we fold up the horizontal line $-\infty abc\infty$ and put it back in the rectilinear figure $ABCD$ in Fig. 18, the pattern drawn in the spongy substance will go back to its old shape.

Sometimes it is convenient to begin with the t-plane and put into it a simple orthogonal system of lines which may be supposed to be drawn on the spongy substance above the axis of ξ. The horizontal line is then supposed to be folded up until it assumes the shape of some rectilinear figure in the z-plane, and the orthogonal system of lines then becomes changed in shape but still remains orthogonal. If now we can find out the relations between the old and the new patterns, we can solve interesting problems relating to electric and magnetic fields bounded by the rectilinear figure in question.

To any little change dz (in passing from a point P to another point very near it) in one plane there corresponds a little change dt in the other plane. We are concerned with the ratio between these two little vectors.

Schwarz and Christoffel have given an expression for this ratio. It takes the form of the following differential equation:

$$\frac{dz}{dt} = K(t-a)^{(\alpha/\pi)-1}(t-b)^{(\beta/\pi)-1}(t-c)^{(\gamma/\pi)-1}\ldots.$$

Here K is an arbitrary constant which may be complex. It is to be determined from the conditions of the problem. The values a, b, c, etc., are the distances (in some agreed units) from the origin in the t-plane of the points that correspond to the corners

E

A, B, C, etc., respectively, in the z-plane. We denote by α, β, γ, etc., the angles at A, B, C, etc., respectively, taken on the inside of the figure ABC ... in Fig. 18.

The reasonableness of this equation may be understood from the following considerations:

Take any point P' in the t-plane whose position is given by the vector $t = \xi + j\eta = m'\epsilon^{j\theta}$.

Imagine that the horizontal line in Fig. 20 represents the trace

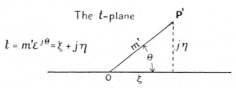

The t-plane

$$t = m'\varepsilon^{j\theta} = \xi + j\eta$$

FIG. 20. The t-plane, bounded by a horizontal line which represents a flat plate above which the hypothetical spongy substance stretches to infinity.

of a flat plate at right angles to the paper, and that the space on the upper side of this plate is filled with a spongy substance, or soap-suds, having the properties described on p. 20. The vector t is supposed to be drawn on a cross-section of that spongy substance. Now imagine the plate folded, at O, along a line at right angles to the paper. The effect will be to diminish the angle θ. For instance, if the horizontal plate is folded at O until the left-hand half stands perpendicular to the right-hand half, we shall get the same transformation as we considered in connexion with Figs. 9 and 10. In this case we had $w = z^2$. The t-plane now takes the place of the w-plane of Fig. 10 so that $z = kt^{\frac{1}{2}}$. Writing $t = m'\epsilon^{j\theta}$ (see Fig. 20), $z = km'\epsilon^{j\theta/2}$ (Fig. 21). That is to say, the argument of z is one-half the argument of t.

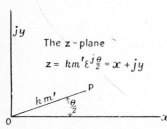

The z-plane

$$z = km'\varepsilon^{j\frac{\theta}{2}} = x + jy$$

FIG. 21. The z-plane, which shows what happens to P when the flat plate is folded at O through a right angle.

The length of the vector is km', where k is an arbitrary constant. In this particular case, the transformation from the t-plane to the z-plane puts no restrictions upon the magnitude of the vector OP.

The parallel lines of Fig. 1 become the curves shown in Fig. 13, but the constant k permits the distance of P from the origin in the z-plane to be what we like. The spongy substance can slide indefinitely along the plane surfaces and, so long as it preserves the pattern shown in Fig. 13, it can change the scale of the pattern indefinitely. As soon as we have fixed the value of k for any point, say $k = k_1$, the scale of the pattern is fixed and the magnitude of the vector to each point is fixed. It is m' in the t-plane and $k_1 m'$ in the z-plane.

The Schwarz-Christoffel equation for the transformation from Fig. 14 to Fig. 13 would be

$$\frac{dz}{dt} = K(t-\mathrm{o})^{(\alpha/\pi)-1} = Kt^{\frac{1}{2}-1},$$

because $\alpha = \frac{1}{2}\pi$, that is, the internal angle at the origin.

$$dz = Kt^{-\frac{1}{2}}\, dt,$$

$$z = 2Kt^{\frac{1}{2}}.$$

If the folding of the horizontal line of the t-plane had not been carried so far, α would be greater and $\alpha/\pi-1$ would be greater. After integration, the -1 of the index disappears so that the new argument in the z-plane becomes α/π. Taking $t = m\epsilon^{j\theta}$ we get now $z = K'm\epsilon^{j\alpha\theta/\pi}$. In a case where α is nearly equal to π, very little compression of the vesicles occurs as we fold the horizontal line. Where α is smaller the compression of the vesicles is greater and the argument in the z-plane is correspondingly reduced.

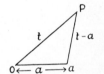

FIG. 22. Showing that the vector drawn from a to P is $(t-a)$.

Now take the case where the folding occurs, not at the origin, but at a point a units away from the origin along the horizontal line in Fig. 22. The vector from the origin to the point P' is t. The vector from a point a units to the right of the origin is $(t-a)$.

Everything that we have said with regard to the raising of t to the $(\alpha/\pi-1)$th power holds except that now we must raise $(t-a)$ to the $(\alpha/\pi-1)$th power, α being the angle of the fold at A in the z-plane. If now there is another corner at B and we imagine the structure of the spongy substance in the t-plane operated upon by a folding of the horizontal line at b, all the vectors $(t-b)$ having their arguments changed in the ratio of π to β, then the ratio dz/dt is further operated upon by the factor $(t-b)^{(\beta/\pi)-1}$; and so on for any number of corners in the figure in the z-plane (see Fig. 18).

The folding up of the horizontal line in the t-plane performs an operation upon any pattern drawn upon the spongy material and affects the ratio of dz to dt. If one folding at a makes the ratio equal to $C_1(t-a)^{(\alpha/\pi)-1}$, then after the folding at b the result will be the product $C_1 C_2 (t-a)^{(\alpha/\pi)-1}(t-b)^{(\beta/\pi)-1}$ and so on.

As the substance never leaves the surface, any point in the straight line ab in the t-plane corresponds with some point in the line AB in the z-plane.

Points on one side of the horizontal axis in the t-plane correspond to points within the polygon on the z-plane and the points a, b, c, etc., correspond to the corners A, B, C, etc.

Now let us see whether the Schwarzian equation gives us the right kind of happening at the corners. For the corner A, $t = a$, and near the corner $(t-a)$ can be made as small as we like without limit. When t is very nearly equal to a let $(t_a-a) = re^{j\theta}$, where r is exceedingly small and θ may be anything from o to π, so that $dt_a = jre^{j\theta}d\theta$, where dt_a is limited to points in the vicinity of a. In changing the value of t as we go past the point a, we may take dt as the radius, of length r, of a little semicircle (shown magnified indefinitely in Fig. 23) and get from one side of a to the other side by changing θ successively through all values between π and o. The only factor in

$$\frac{dz}{dt} = K(t_a-a)^{(\alpha/\pi)-1}(a-b)^{(\beta/\pi)-1}(a-c)^{(\gamma/\pi)-1}...$$

which gives rise to a change in the argument of dz/dt is the factor $(t_a-a)^{(\alpha/\pi)-1}$. Here we have written a instead of t_a in all the brackets except the first because, in comparison with b, c, etc., $t_a = a$. A point such as b being a finite distance from a, no change of argument occurs in (t_a-b) when t_a is nearly equal to a. This is because r is infinitely short and when it is swung round from π to o the vector (t_a-b) or $(a-b)$ does not alter its direction and is constant.

We may write $\qquad \dfrac{dz}{dt_a} = C(t_a-a)^{(\alpha/\pi)-1},$

$dz = C\{re^{j\theta}\}^{(\alpha/\pi)-1}\,dt_a$, where dt_a is limited to points in the vicinity of a.

$$dz = jCr^{(\alpha/\pi)-1}\,\epsilon^{j\theta\{(\alpha/\pi)-1\}}\,re^{j\theta}\,d\theta = jCr^{\alpha/\pi}\,\epsilon^{j\theta\alpha/\pi}\,d\theta.$$

From this we see that when θ, the argument of dt, changes from π to o, the argument of dz changes from α to o. This is exactly what is wanted in order that the point a in the straight horizontal line shall correspond with the corner A containing the angle α.

It will be seen that though a change in the argument of dz/dt occurs when the end of the vector t crosses an angle point such as a or b, no such change occurs so long as the end of the vector moves between two angle points along the horizontal line that cor-

FIG. 23. The passing of the value of t past the point a by way of a semicircle of infinitely small radius, r.

responds to one of the sides of the rectangle such as the line ab. The Schwarzian equation gives us this result because all the vectors $(t-a)$, $(t-b)$, etc. lie in the real axis in the t-plane and any argument in the complex constant K remains constant. Under the above conditions there is no change in the argument of dz. This is to say that while t moves in a straight line along the horizontal axis, say from a to b, z also moves along a straight line, say from A to B, so that points in the real axis ξ correspond to points in the boundaries of the rectilinear figure in the z-plane. As soon, however, as the end of the vector t moves to a point above the horizontal axis, the argument of dt changes and the argument of dz also changes in a manner prescribed by the equation.

A rough idea of how the Schwarzian equation operates can be obtained from Figs. 24 and 25 which are intended to show a small change in the t-plane and a corresponding change in the z-plane. When the end of the vector t is at P', the vectors $(t-a)$, $(t-b)$, and $(t-c)$ are as illustrated. Each of these could be expressed in the form $m_a \epsilon^{j\theta_a}$, $m_b \epsilon^{j\theta_b}$, $m_c \epsilon^{j\theta_c}$. The raising of these complex quantities to the powers $(\alpha/\pi - 1)$, $(\beta/\pi - 1)$, and $(\gamma/\pi - 1)$ respectively, changes both the magnitudes m and the arguments $\epsilon^{j\theta}$. Now the Schwarzian equation tells us that the ratio between the little vectors dz and dt, is equal to the product of these changed vectors into the constant K. The amount of bending at each of the angles determines the value of the changed vector for that angle. Whenever the bending angle is less than π the index comes out negative so that instead of multiplying by $(t-a)$, $(t-b)$, etc., we are dividing by some power of these vectors. This makes dz

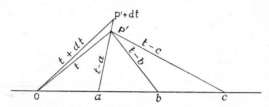

FIG. 24. A small change in the position of P' and its effect on $(t-a)$, $(t-b)$, etc.

less than dt. When the angle is greater than π the index is positive, and this tends to make dz greater than dt. This is exactly what we should expect from the behaviour of the spongy material (see p. 27). Take the case where the z-plane is identical with the t-plane, that is to say, when there is no bending at angles. Each of the above indices would be equal to o so that all the factors would be equal to unity if the z- and t-planes were drawn to the same scale.

We make use of the Schwarzian transformation as follows: It is required to find the distribution of a field of force bounded by equipotential surfaces (or it may be by stream-line surfaces) whose projections on the z-plane make a rectilinear figure.

Our inquiry is limited to the kind of distribution which varies with x and y but not in a direction at right angles to the plane x, y. Further, this two-dimensional field is supposed to satisfy the conditions laid down on p. 15.

(1) We begin by transforming the rectilinear figure into a straight line along the axis of ξ in the t-plane, that is, we get the Schwarzian relation between z and t. (2) Then noting which

parts of the axis of ξ correspond to the equipotential surfaces (or stream-lines as the case may be) in the problem, we put into the t-plane a field of force having its equipotential surfaces (or stream-line surfaces) on the said corresponding parts in the t-plane. This gives us the distribution expressed as a function of t,

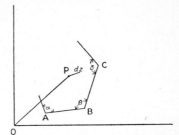

$$\phi+j\psi = f(t) = f(\xi+j\eta).$$

FIG. 25. A small change in the position of P in the z-plane and the effect of folding the horizontal line *oabc* of the t-plane at A, B, etc. through the angles, α, β, etc.

(3) Now the Schwarzian equation gives us the relation between t and z, say $t = F(z)$. Substituting for t its equivalent in z, we get an expression for the distribution that we should get in the z-plane if we folded up the equipotential surfaces (as described on p. 25) and put them at the angles to one another that are required in the original problem. This gives us

$$\phi+j\psi = f\{F(z)\}.$$

Now it may be that we cannot easily see how to put into the t-plane a distribution that fits the equipotential surfaces in question. To help us, we may make use of the same kind of transformation. Take a new plane, say the w-plane, into which we can put a very simple field, say like that depicted in Fig. 1, with very simple boundaries. Imagine the w-equipotentials opened out into the t-plane. By the Schwarzian transformation find the relation between w and t. We arrange matters so that the new distribution in the t-plane has suitable equipotential lines (or stream-lines) to correspond with those in the z-plane. Then we are in a position to fold up the t-equipotentials to fit the distribution in the z-plane.

We will take first some examples in which the answer is already known so that a student can see how the process is operating. This may appear to be a repetition of what we have given before, but it is now given as an example of the Schwarzian method of attack upon a familiar problem.

EXAMPLE NO. I

STREAM-LINES ROUND A CORNER

IT is desired to find the equations of the stream-lines and equipotential lines near the corner of a very large square sheet of conducting material, where one of the stream-lines follows the edge round the right-angled corner.

This is the same problem as we considered on p. 13, but here we propose to solve it by the Schwarzian method.

In Fig. 26 the axes of x and y represent the corner of the square in question. One of the stream-lines of the current is along x and

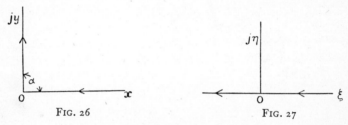

FIG. 26   FIG. 27

FIG. 26. A right angle at O in the z-plane.

FIG. 27. The effect of opening out the right angle into a straight horizontal line.

round the corner and then along y as shown. Open out this rectilinear figure into a straight horizontal line in the t-plane (Fig. 27). In this case it is convenient to let the origin in the z-plane fall on the origin in the t-plane.

From p. 25 we get

$$\frac{dz}{dt} = A(t-0)^{(\alpha/\pi)-1},$$

where A is an arbitrary constant and $\alpha = \frac{1}{2}\pi$, so that

$$dz = At^{-\frac{1}{2}}\, dt.$$

Integrating, $z = 2At^{\frac{1}{2}} + \text{constant.}$

By fixing the values (see p. 34) so that the constant vanishes,

$$t = \frac{1}{4A^2}\, z^2.$$

Now put into the t-plane a simple parallel flow of current such that one of the stream-lines lies along the axis of ξ which corresponds to the stream-line distribution shown in Fig. 1,

$$V+jC = K(\xi+j\eta) = Kt \quad \text{(see p. 10)}.$$

K is the current per cm. width of path flowing in a sheet whose resistance is 1 ohm per sq. cm. Thus

$$V+jC = \frac{K}{4A^2}(x+jy)^2$$

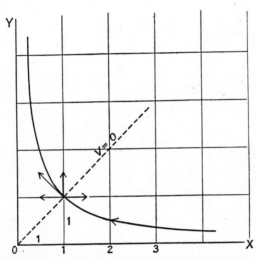

FIG. 28. Stream-lines of current flowing round a corner of a conducting sheet. Method of determining the value of K_2.

gives the distribution of potential and current functions in the z-plane.

The value of the constant $K/4A^2$ can be found in any particular case where the current density at any point of the square is known. This is shown later. For the moment we will call it K_2. Then as on p. 16,

$$V = K_2(x^2-y^2),$$

$$C = K_2\, 2xy.$$

The stream-lines are rectangular hyperbolae asymptotic to the axes of x and y. The equipotential lines (shown dotted in Fig. 13) are also rectangular hyperbolae, but these are asymptotic to a line at $45°$ to the axes of x and y. It is convenient to take the line at $45°$ as the equipotential line whose value is zero, because this makes the arbitrary constant of integration equal to zero. On the $45°$ line $x_1 = y_1$, therefore

$$V = K_2(x_1^2 - y_1^2) = 0.$$

To find the value of K_2 we must have further data given. Suppose that at the point $x = 1$, $y = 1$ (Fig. 28) the current density (amperes per cm. width of path) is i_1. The direction is at right angles to the $V = 0$ line, that is, at $45°$ to the axes of x and y. The current density is the vector sum of $\partial C/\partial x$ and $\partial C/\partial y$.

Since $C = 2K_2 xy$,

$$\frac{\partial C}{\partial x} = 2K_2 y \quad \text{and} \quad \frac{\partial C}{\partial y} = 2K_2 x.$$

Writing $x = 1$ and $y = 1$ and taking the vector sum of two quantities at right angles, we get

$$2\sqrt{2}\, K_2 = i_1. \qquad \therefore\ K_2 = \frac{i_1}{2\sqrt{2}}.$$

It is well that the student should practise, at this stage, shifting the origin, so as to see what effect it has on the final result. Take the easy case where the origin in the z-plane is not at the corner, as in Fig. 26, but at a point, say B, some distance to the right of the origin. Let the corresponding distance in the t-plane be denoted by b, where b is wholly real. We have

$$\frac{dz}{dt} = A(t-b)^{-\frac{1}{2}},$$

$$\therefore\ z = 2A(t-b)^{\frac{1}{2}} + \text{const.}$$

When $z = 0$, let $t = b$, so that the arbitrary constant vanishes as before.

$$t = \frac{z^2}{4A^2} + b,$$

$$V + jC = K\frac{z^2}{4A^2} + Kb,$$

$$V = \frac{K}{4A^2}(x^2 - y^2) + Kb,$$

$$C = \frac{K}{2A^2}xy.$$

Since b is wholly real, the Kb term does not affect C.

EXAMPLE NO. 2

THE CASE OF A SINGLE SINK

THE DISTRIBUTION OF STREAM-LINES AND EQUIPOTENTIAL LINES
IN A THIN CONDUCTING SHEET INTO WHICH CURRENT IS FED AT
AN INFINITE BOUNDARY AND FROM WHICH IT IS TAKEN AT A
POINT CALLED THE SINK. IN PRACTICE THE SINK MAY BE CIRCULAR
AND OF FINITE SIZE WITHOUT AFFECTING THE DISTRIBUTION.

THE problem has been already dealt with on p. 4 and the solution arrived at without having recourse to the Schwarzian transformation. The object in repeating it here is that the student may see how the Schwarzian transformation gives a result with which he is already familiar.

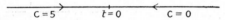

$$C = 5 \qquad t = 0 \qquad C = 0$$

FIG. 29. The boundary stream-lines of a current of 5 amperes flowing in a semicircular sheet to the point $t = 0$ acting as a sink.

Consider first the case of a parallel flow of current in the z-plane as in Fig. 1. Here we have $V+jC = k(x+jy) = kz$. Imagine all the parallel lines of this figure drawn on the spongy material as described on p. 19, and the lines $C = 0$ and $C = 5$ adjacent to solid surfaces and attached in the manner there mentioned. Now bring the left-hand ends of these surfaces together and the right-hand ends further apart as shown in Fig. 15. Continue the opening-out of the surfaces until the line $C = 5$ makes an angle of 180° with the line $C = 0$ as shown in Fig. 29.

It will be noted that the stream-line $C = 5$ which is attached to the upper surface in Fig. 1 is now placed in a reverse position so that the direction of flow along it is from left to right in Fig. 29. The two stream-lines $C = 0$ and $C = 5$ now correspond to the stream-lines $C = 0$ and $C = 5$ in Fig. 30, which is supposed to represent the uniform flow of a current of 10 amperes from the external circle to the centre point or sink S. The upper half of Fig. 30 will correspond in all particulars to the region above the horizontal line in Fig. 29 if we imagine the circle in Fig. 30 made infinitely large. Therefore, when Fig. 1 is transformed into

Fig. 29 the parallel flow of current in Fig. 1 is transformed into a flow from the outer regions of an infinite sheet towards a sink except that the region above the horizontal line in Fig. 29 only contains half the current that flows in the infinite sheet.

Now let us apply the Schwarzian differential equation to this simple case. Fig. 1 is to be taken as the plane of z and Fig. 29 as the plane of t. Let the point where the two left ends of the lines in Fig. 1 (or Fig. 14) meet in Fig. 29 be taken as zero ($t = 0$) in the t-plane.

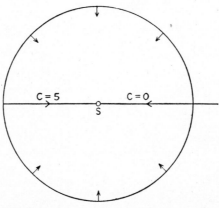

Fig. 30. A current of 10 amperes in a large sheet converging on the sink S.

The reader will note that the distribution to be studied is here put into the t-plane while the parallel flow is in the z-plane. This is opposite to the procedure in Example No. 1.

From p. 25 we have

$$\frac{dz}{dt} = A(t-0)^{(0/\pi)-1} = A\frac{1}{t}.$$

Note that the angle between the upper line ($C = 5$) and the lower line ($C = 0$) in Fig. 1 is zero.

$$\frac{dz}{dt} = A(t-0)^{(0/\pi)-1},$$

$$\int dz = A \int \frac{1}{t}\, dt,$$

$$z = A \log t = V + jC.$$

Let $t = r\epsilon^{j\theta}$, $A \log t = A \log r + Aj\theta.$

In the above, the integration constant is dealt with as shown below.

Equating real and imaginary parts of the equation,

$$V = A \log r,$$

$$C = A\theta.$$

To find the value of A to suit the case where the current in the half infinite plane is 5 amperes, we note that when $\theta = \pi$, $C = 5$,

$$5 = A\pi. \qquad \therefore \quad A = \frac{5}{\pi}.$$

$$V + jC = \frac{5}{\pi} \log r + j\frac{5}{\pi}\theta.$$

The equipotential lines are circles, and to find the potential of any circle we multiply the logarithm of the radius by $5/\pi$. This is on the assumption that we take the circle $r = 1$ at zero potential, and thus eliminate the constant of integration.

In some problems it is necessary to have the sink S, not at the point $t = 0$ but at the point $t = a$.

We then have

$$\frac{dz}{dt} = A(t-a)^{(0/\pi)-1} = \frac{A}{t-a},$$

$$z = A \int \frac{dt}{t-a} = A \log(t-a) + C.$$

If we now have the condition $z = 0$ when $t = a+1$ we eliminate the arbitrary constant C.

When $(t-a) = 1+j0$ we have $\theta = 0$, so that the line of zero stream-function is the horizontal line drawn from a to the right. Putting $(t-a) = re^{j\theta}$ and assuming that $C = 5$ when $\theta = \pi$,

$$V + jC = \frac{5}{\pi} \log r + j\frac{5}{\pi}\theta$$

as before, but now r and θ get their values from $(t-a)$ instead of from t.

EXAMPLE NO. 3

SOURCE AND SINK IN A PLANE

THE DISTRIBUTION OF STREAM-LINES AND EQUIPOTENTIAL LINES
IN A THIN CONDUCTING SHEET INTO WHICH CURRENT IS FED AT
A POINT SOURCE AND OUT OF WHICH IT IS TAKEN AT A POINT
SINK.

IT is shown below that all the stream-lines are parts of circles
and that the equipotentials are also circles cutting the first
named at right angles.

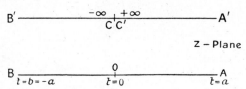

FIG. 31. The z-plane to be opened out to form a source and a sink.

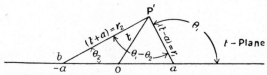

FIG. 32. The vectors of P' from the source and sink, $(t-a)$ and $(t+a)$.

To get an expression for the positions of these circles we will
transform the two parallel lines on the z-plane in Fig. 31 into
one horizontal line on the t-plane as in Fig. 32.

Instead of opening out the lines as we did in connexion with
Fig. 14 we will break the line $B'A'$ at the middle point C and open
out $C'A'$ towards the right making the point C' correspond to
$+\infty$ in the t-plane, and open out CB' to the left making C
correspond to $-\infty$ in the t-plane. The point a in the t-plane
corresponds to the point where A and A' converge and the point
b or $-a$ corresponds to the point where B and B' converge.
Fig. 31 being symmetrical, $b = -a$. Note that the internal
angles at A and at B are zero so that $\alpha/\pi = 0$ and $\beta/\pi = 0$.

The Schwarzian transformation tells that

$$\frac{dz}{dt} = K(t-a)^{-1}(t+a)^{-1} = K\frac{1}{t^2-a^2},$$

$$\int dz = K \int \frac{dt}{t^2 - a^2},$$

$$z = \frac{K}{2a} \log \frac{t-a}{t+a} + K_2.$$

Take any point P' in the t-plane. The vector OP' is t and the vector drawn from a to P' is $(t-a)$.

Let the length of this be r_1 and its angle be θ_1, so that

$$(t-a) = r_1 \epsilon^{j\theta_1}.$$

Similarly, let the vector drawn from $-a$ to $P' = (t+a) = r_2 \epsilon^{j\theta_2}$. Then (merging $1/2a$ in the arbitrary constant K_1) we have

$$z = K_1 \log \frac{r_1 \epsilon^{j\theta_1}}{r_2 \epsilon^{j\theta_2}} + K_2 = K_1 \left\{ \log \frac{r_1}{r_2} + j(\theta_1 - \theta_2) \right\} + K_2.$$

Now imagine a parallel current stream put into the z-plane as described in connexion with Fig. 1 and let the sheet of metal in the z-plane have the properties described on p. 2 so that

$$z = V + jC \text{ as on p. 10.}$$

After the transformation described above we have

$$V + jC = K_1 \left\{ \log \frac{r_1}{r_2} + j(\theta_1 - \theta_2) \right\} + K_2.$$

The locus of a point which gives a constant ratio r_1/r_2 is a circle, as shown in Fig. 33, so that each value of

$$V = K_1 \log \frac{r_1}{r_2}$$

gives an equipotential circle. When the ratio $r_1/r_2 = 1$ we get $\log(r_1/r_2) = 0$, and this gives the line of zero potential as a vertical medial line, assuming that we take no real component in the constant K_2.

The angle at the apex of the triangle in Fig. 32 is $\theta_1 - \theta_2$ and the locus that keeps this constant is the arc of a circle. We see, therefore, that the stream-lines of current are arcs of circles passing through the source and the sink at a and $-a$ (see Figs. 32 and 33).

In order to evaluate the constants K_1 and K_2 we must know the value of the total current in the strip of metal (Fig. 31). Let this be $I/2$ flowing from right to left. Along the line AB the value of the stream function $C = 0$ and this corresponds to ab in Fig. 32 and $S_1 S_2$ in Fig. 33. Along the line $A'C'$ (which corresponds to the horizontal line from a to infinity on the right) the value of C is $I/2$.

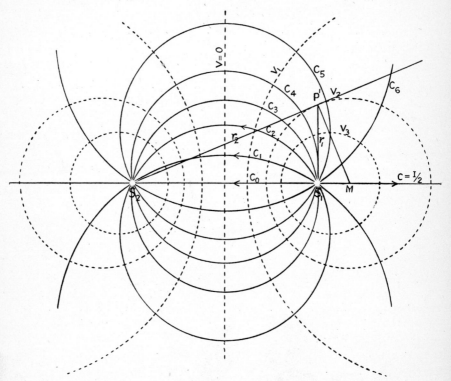

FIG. 33. Stream-lines of current flowing from a source to a sink in an infinite sheet. Also equipotential lines shown as dotted circles.

On the horizontal line to the right of a both θ_1 and $\theta_2 = 0$, therefore, on this line,

$$jC = jI/2 = K_1 j(0-0) + K_2,$$

$$K_2 = jI/2.$$

Filling in this value for the conditions on ab,

$$jC = 0 = K_1 j(\pi - 0) + jI/2,$$

$$K_1 = -\frac{I}{2\pi}.$$

The expression for the voltage and current distribution in Fig. 33 thus becomes

$$V+jC = -\frac{I}{2\pi}\log\frac{r_1}{r_2} - j\frac{I}{2\pi}(\theta_1-\theta_2) + j\frac{I}{2}.$$

It should be noted that in Fig. 33 the current $I/2$ flows wholly above the horizontal line. If we were dealing with the case of an infinite sheet containing a source and a sink the total current being I, this is double the current taken in the strip in Fig. 31. The formula is given in a form which is correct when I is the

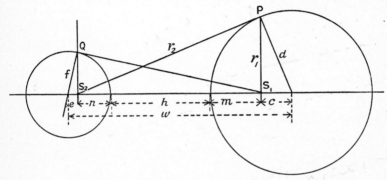

FIG. 34. For finding the positions of S_1 and S_2 when two equipotential circles are given.

current supplied to the source and taken out at the sink in an infinite sheet, having the resistance characteristic given on p. 2.

The various equipotential circles in Fig. 33 have their centres at various points along the horizontal line. If a tangent S_2P is drawn from the sink S_2 to any circle on the right of the medial line as in Fig. 34, the polar PS_1 passes through the source S_1. Similarly, a tangent from S_1 to the circle on the left gives the polar QS_2, which passes through the sink S_2. Let w be the distance between the centres of any two circles, then from the similarity of right-angled triangles

$$\frac{c}{d} = \frac{d}{w-e} = \frac{r_1}{r_2},$$

$$\frac{e}{f} = \frac{f}{w-c} = \frac{r_2'}{r_1'} = \frac{S_2Q}{S_1Q},$$

$$d^2 = cw - ec,$$

G

$$f^2 = ew - ec,$$

$$d^2 - f^2 = w(c - e),$$

$$e = c - \frac{d^2 - f^2}{w}.$$

Eliminating e we get a quadratic in c in terms of w, d, and f.

$$c = \frac{w^2 + d^2 - f^2 \pm \sqrt{(f^2 - d^2 - w^2)^2 - 4w^2 d^2}}{2w}.$$

If we are given any two circles having the radii d and f respectively and having their centres at a distance of w, we can find the positions of S_1 and S_2, the source and sink in an infinite sheet, which will make the circles equipotential circles. Of the two roots to the above equation the smaller (marked c in Fig. 34) is the distance of S_1 from the centre of the larger circle and the larger is the distance of the sink S_2 from the same centre.

EXAMPLE NO. 4

CASES WHERE THE EQUIPOTENTIAL SURFACES OR STREAM-LINE BOUNDARIES ARE CIRCLES.

THE simplest cases are where the circular surfaces can be fitted into a known orthogonal system in which the equipotential surfaces are circular. Such a case is given in the following example:

Two circular cylinders of copper, 3 metres long, stand vertically in a solution of copper sulphate, whose resistivity is

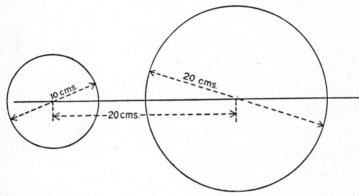

FIG. 35. Two equipotential circles representing two copper cylinders in a bath of electrolyte, or two ferromagnetic cylinders in air with a magnetic field between them.

50 ohms between opposite sides of a cubic centimetre. One cylinder is 20 cm. in diameter and the other 10 cm. The distance between the centres is 20 cm. Find the resistance to the flow of current from one cylinder to the other on the assumption that the bath is very large.

The surfaces of the cylinders will be equipotential surfaces and will form part of an orthogonal system like that depicted in Fig. 33. If we can find the positions of the source S_1 and sink S_2 in an infinite sheet, which would give equipotential lines corresponding to these circles, we can write down the expression for the distribution of stream-lines and equipotentials in terms of the vectors drawn from S_1 and S_2. We might fill the values

$$w = 20, \qquad d = 10, \qquad f = 5,$$

in the formula on p. 42.

But we note that all these numbers are divisible by 5, and we know that the result will be the same as if we took

$$w = 4, \qquad d = 2, \qquad f = 1,$$

for these figures will give the same ratio of r_1/r_2 in the final formula. Thus for the larger circle

$$c = \frac{16+4-1\pm\sqrt{19^2-4\times16\times4}}{2\times4}$$

$$= 1\cdot096 \text{ or } 3\cdot655.$$

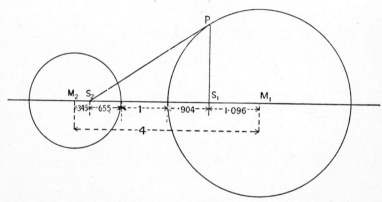

FIG. 36. Showing the positions of S_1 and S_2 for the circles given in Fig. 35.

This gives the distances of S_1 and S_2 from the centre M_1 of the large circle.

Or we might have calculated the distances from the centre M_2 of the smaller circle

$$e = \frac{16+1-4\pm\sqrt{13^2-4\times16}}{8}$$

$$= 0\cdot345 \text{ or } 2\cdot904.$$

The positions of M_1, M_2, S_1, and S_2 are shown in Fig. 36. Thus we see that $r_1/r_2 = \dfrac{0\cdot904}{1\cdot655} = 0\cdot548$ for the large circle, and

$$\frac{r_1'}{r_2'} = \frac{1\cdot904}{0\cdot655} = 2\cdot905.$$

The resistance between opposite sides of a cubic centimetre of the solution is given as 50 ohms. Let us consider a depth of bath of 50 cm. Each sq. cm. of horizontal area of the bath will then be strictly comparable with the sheet of metal considered on p. 2. That is, it will have a resistance of 1 ohm between opposite sides of 1 sq. cm. For this depth of bath a current density (see note on p. 3) of 1 ampere per cm. gives a drop of 1 volt per cm. length of path.

Now imagine a current of 1 ampere passing from 50 cm. length of the larger copper cylinder to 50 cm. of the shorter cylinder. From p. 41,

$$V + jC = -\frac{1}{2\pi}\left(\log\frac{r_1}{r_2}\right) - j\frac{1}{2\pi}(\theta_1 - \theta_2) + j\tfrac{1}{2}.$$

To find the voltage between the cylinders under those conditions, fill in the values of r_1/r_2.

For the larger cylinder $V_1 = -(1/2\pi)\log 0\cdot 548$

$= 0\cdot 0959.$

For the small cylinder $V_2 = -(1/2\pi)\log 2\cdot 905$

$= -0\cdot 170.$

Therefore the difference of potential between the two cylinders is $0\cdot 2659$ volts. As 1 ampere is passing per 50 cm. length of cylinder, this is the resistance of a bath 50 cm. deep. But the bath is 3 metres deep, therefore the resistance of the whole bath is

$$0\cdot 2659 \div 6 = 0\cdot 0443 \text{ ohms}.$$

The same method can be used to measure the magnetic reluctance between two round pole shanks such as the main pole and the commutating pole of a dynamo. If we assume, in the first instance, that the surface of each pole is at a uniform magnetic potential, we shall get a resultant leakage flux which is twice as great as the leakage flux with the magnetic potential varying uniformly from zero to its maximum value. Where the poles in practice are not parallel, the error of the method can be minimized by making three separate calculations for three different centres of circles and at suitable differences of magnetic potential and plotting the results in a curve whose mean ordinate will give the average leakage per cm. length of pole.

EXAMPLE NO. 5

THE FLOW OF CURRENT ROUND TWO RIGHT-ANGLED CORNERS

CONSIDER the flow of an electric current in a sheet of metal of uniform thickness and resistivity such as shown in Fig. 37 having two right-angled corners at A and B and appropriate equipotential lines CD and EF, and also a stream-line edge DE (whose proper shape will appear as the investigation proceeds). Current is fed in at CD and taken out at EF. The edges of the rectangular strip $CABF$ form one stream-line. It is required to find expressions for the equipotential lines and also for the stream-lines throughout the whole sheet. The method of attack is applicable to a strip of metal of indefinite length along AC

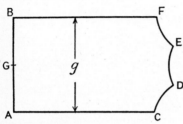

Fig. 37. Sheet of metal with current fed in at CD and out at EF given a stream-line along $CABF$.

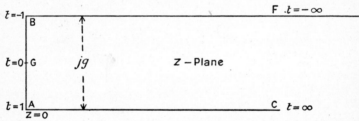

Fig. 38. The z-plane showing the corresponding points in the t-plane.

which is taken as the axis of x in the z-plane. The width of the strip AB is finite and equal to g.

To make the problem perfectly general we will take the boundaries AC and BF as if they extended to infinity as shown in Fig. 38.

The first step is to transform the stream-line $CABF$ (which is in the z-plane) into a straight line in the t-plane. It is convenient to take G, the mid-point between A and B, to correspond to the origin in the t-plane.

Starting with the Schwarzian equation

$$\frac{dz}{dt} = K(t-a)^{(\alpha/\pi)-1}(t-b)^{(\beta/\pi)-1},$$

the angle at A is $\frac{1}{2}\pi$ so that the index $(\alpha/\pi-1)$ becomes $(\frac{1}{2}-1) = -\frac{1}{2}$. The angle at B is also $\frac{1}{2}\pi$ and gives rise to the index $-\frac{1}{2}$ for the $(t-b)$ term. As the scale in the t-plane is not fixed, we can simplify matters by taking the point a as being a unit distance from the origin, so that $a = 1$ and $b = -1$. We then get

$$\frac{dz}{dt} = K(t+1)^{-\frac{1}{2}}(t-1)^{-\frac{1}{2}} = K\frac{1}{\sqrt{t^2-1}}.$$

At $t = \infty$ the passage from one end of the horizontal straight

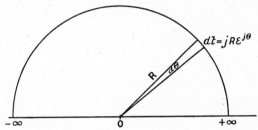

FIG. 39. Showing the passage of t from $+\infty$ to $-\infty$ over a semicircle of infinite radius.

line to the other (corresponding to the passage from C to F in the z-plane) is carried out at the end of an infinite radius R which turns from $\theta = 0$ to $\theta = \pi$ (see Fig. 39 in which R is supposed to be infinite). During this passage t occupies successively all the positions of the radius and may be written $t = Re^{j\theta}$, where θ changes from $\theta = 0$ to $\theta = \pi$.

A little change in t, that is dt, is obviously at right angles to t

$$dt = jRe^{j\theta}\, d\theta.$$

This is obtained by differentiation and can be seen to be true from Fig. 39.

We can find the value of K by integrating* dz across the strip of width g.

$$jg = \int_C^F dz = K\frac{1}{\sqrt{t^2-1}} \times jRe^{j\theta} \int_0^\pi d\theta.$$

* It is shown below that, whatever the value of K may be, the constant of integration is zero for the case where $t = 1$ when $z = 0$.

Since t is infinite in this special case,

$$\frac{1}{\sqrt{t^2-1}} \div \frac{1}{t} = \frac{1}{Re^{j\theta}},$$

and this cancels out with the $Re^{j\theta}$ above the line, so that

$$jg = jK\pi,$$
$$K = g/\pi,$$

$$\frac{dz}{dt} = \frac{g}{\pi} \frac{1}{\sqrt{t^2-1}}.$$

Integrating, we get $z = \frac{g}{\pi}\cosh^{-1}t + A_1,$

that is, $\cosh\left(\frac{\pi z}{g} - A_2\right) = t.$

Let $t = 1$ when $z = 0$, then as $\cosh 0 = 1$, we get $A_2 = 0$ and thus eliminate the constant of integration. We shall see in a subsequent example that by giving a different value to A_2 we can shift the position of the point corresponding to $z = 0$ (see p. 68).

Another method of arriving at the value of K is as follows:

$$z = K\cosh^{-1}t.$$

From Fig. 38 we see that when t changes from -1 to $+1$, z changes by jg.

$$\therefore \quad jg = K\{\cosh^{-1}(-1) - \cosh^{-1}(+1)\}$$
$$= K\{j\pi - 0\} \quad \text{(see p. 57)}$$
$$= jK\pi.$$

$$\therefore \quad K = \frac{g}{\pi}.$$

This method is simpler than the one given before, but the method of integrating over the infinite semicircle will be found useful in many problems, and is therefore given above.

Now imagine that in the t-plane we have a simple rectangular arrangement of stream-lines of current and equipotential lines (as in Fig. 40), so that

$$t = V + jC,$$

$$\cosh\frac{\pi z}{g} = V + jC.$$

Since $z = x + jy$,

$$\cosh\frac{\pi z}{g} = \cosh\frac{\pi x}{g}\cos\frac{\pi y}{g} + j\sinh\frac{\pi x}{g}\sin\frac{\pi y}{g}.$$

The real part

$$\cosh\frac{\pi x}{g}\cos\frac{\pi y}{g} = V,$$

and

$$\sinh\frac{\pi x}{g}\sin\frac{\pi y}{g} = C.$$

Now let us find how the straight lines $V = 0$, $V = 1$, etc., in the

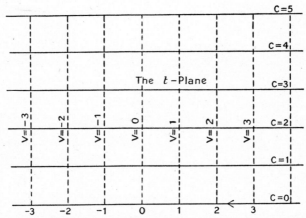

FIG. 40. Parallel distribution of current in the *t*-plane, $t = V + jC$.

t-plane are distorted when the *t*-plane is folded at the two points $t = 1$ and $t = -1$ so as to make the *z*-plane.

When $V = 0$,

$$\cosh\frac{\pi x}{g}\cos\frac{\pi y}{g} = 0.$$

We know that $\cosh\dfrac{\pi x}{g}$ can never be equal to zero so that $\cos\dfrac{\pi y}{g} = 0$

or $\pi y/g = \frac{1}{2}\pi$, that is,* $y = g/2$.

Thus the vertical line $V = 0$ in the *t*-plane (see Fig. 40) becomes in the *z*-plane a horizontal line parallel to the axis of x at a height $g/2$ above that axis.

Similarly we can find that the lower end of the line that corresponds to $V = 1$ starts from the point $z = 0$.

* Strictly $\pi y/g = \frac{1}{2}n\pi$, where $n = 1, 3, 5$, etc. We are only concerned with the region where $n = 1$.

For
$$V = 1 = \cosh\frac{\pi x}{g}\cos\frac{\pi y}{g}.$$

When $x = 0$,
$$\cosh\frac{\pi x}{g} = 1,$$

and when $y = 0$,
$$\cos\frac{\pi y}{g} = 1.$$

In order to trace the curve $V = 1$ in the z-plane, it is convenient to use Kennelly's *Tables of Complex Hyperbolic and Circular Functions.** The values of hyperbolic cosines are given for different values of $x + jq$, where $q = 2y/\pi$. That is to say that q is in quadrants when y is in radians. As the values of the hyperbolic sines and cosines are periodic and repeat themselves as jy passes through increments of $j2\pi$, by making $q = 2y/\pi$ we shall have the tables repeating themselves as jq passes through increments of $j4$. Moreover, there is merely a change in sign as jq passes through increments of $j2$. Thus the tables need only be given up to $q = 2$ and serve for any value of y or q.

It so happens that these tables are very convenient for plotting the curves of constant values of either the real or the unreal part of $\cosh\frac{\pi z}{g}$. The values come out most simply for the case where $g = 2$. For then we have

$$\cosh\frac{\pi z}{g} = \cosh\left(\frac{\pi x}{g} + j\frac{\pi y}{g}\right) = \cosh\left(\frac{\pi}{2}x + j\frac{\pi}{2}y\right).$$

Thus when $y = 1$ radian, the expression $\frac{1}{2}\pi y$ gives enough radians to make one quadrant. So that if instead of multiplying the values of y by $\frac{1}{2}\pi$ we simply substitute the value of y for the expression $\frac{1}{2}\pi y$ we get the value of $\frac{1}{2}\pi y$ expressed in quadrants. The tables are then directly applicable (except that x must still keep its coefficient $\frac{1}{2}\pi$).

Beginning at the point in the tables where $x = 0$ and $q = 0$, the real part of the value of the hyperbolic cosine $= 1$, that is, $V = 1$. Now follow through the tables for higher values of x and q that give the real part of the cosh equal to unity.

* Harvard University Press.

These will be found to be those given in the table below:

$\dfrac{\pi x}{g}$	y
0	0
0·2	0·149
0·4	0·258
0·6	0·362
0·8	0·465
1·0	0·550
1·2	0·628
1·4	0·693
1·6	0·745
1·8	0·795
2·0	0·828
2·58	0·900
3·24	0·950

Suppose now that g has the value 16 cm. instead of 2. It is evident that x and y will have to be 8 times as great in order that $\cosh(\pi z/g)$ shall have the values 1, 2, or 3 when plotting the curves $V = 1$, $V = 2$, or $V = 3$. It is therefore only necessary to multiply the values in the above table by 8 in order to get the values of the ordinates of the curve $V = 1$, as plotted in Fig. 41 for the case of a strip of metal 16 cm. wide. Similarly we can plot the curve $V = 2$ by starting from the point $\dfrac{\pi x}{g} = 1\cdot317$ and $q = 0$. For $\dfrac{\pi x}{g} = 1\cdot4$ and $q = 0\cdot23$ we get another point on the curve and so on.

The equipotential lines for various values of V are plotted in Fig. 41. The stream-lines are shown in this figure with full lines.*

The stream-line $C = 1$ is plotted by taking various values of $\sinh\dfrac{\pi x}{g}$ in the expression

$$\sinh\frac{\pi x}{g} \cdot \sin\frac{\pi y}{g} = 1$$

and working out the values of x and y. In Fig. 41 the y-ordinates

* The author is indebted to Mr. J. T. Birtwell for the work of calculating and plotting Fig. 41.

have been converted into *q*-values and plotted to the scale of $g/2 = 8$. In the first instance we may take $g = 2$ and then multiply the ordinates by 8.

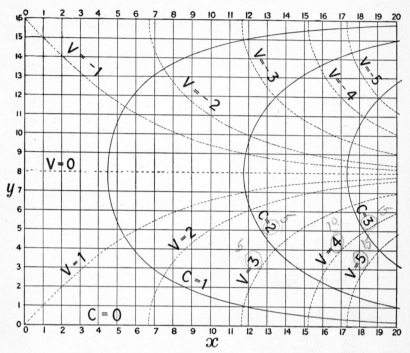

FIG. 41. Distribution of stream-lines and equipotential lines as a current goes round two right angles in a uniform strip of conducting material.

Here again we can make use of Kennelly's *Tables*, but we find the values of $\dfrac{\pi x}{g}$ and *q* that make the coefficient of the unreal term in $\cosh \dfrac{\pi z}{g}$ equal to unity, and so on for the curve $C = 2$.

In order to get, in practice, a distribution of current and potential like that shown in Fig. 41, a sheet of uniformly resisting material should be cut out like Fig. 37, in which *CD* and *EF* are made to fit two of the equipotential lines in Fig. 41, and *DE* follows a stream-line. In feeding in the current and taking it out *CD* must be kept at a uniform potential, as also *EF*.

EXAMPLE NO. 6

SUDDEN REDUCTION IN WIDTH OF CHANNEL

THE FLOW OF CURRENT AROUND TWO RIGHT-ANGLED BENDS, ONE
EXTERNAL AND THE OTHER INTERNAL. THE PASSAGE OF MAG-
NETIC FLUX ACROSS AN AIR-GAP WHOSE LENGTH CHANGES FROM
ONE VALUE TO ANOTHER AS WE MOVE AT RIGHT ANGLES TO THE
FLUX.

THE next case to be considered is that of a current flowing
in a strip of metal of uniform thickness whose width changes
suddenly from c to g as shown in Fig. 42. The solution of this

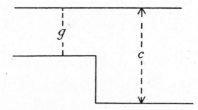

FIG. 42. A strip of metal having a width g at one part and a greater
width c at another. The passage from c to g forms two right angles, one
internal and the other external, so that an electric current passing along
the strip must go round these right angles.

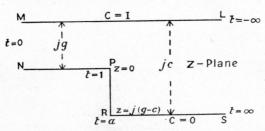

FIG. 43. The z-plane corresponding to the strip in Fig. 42, showing the
points that correspond to points in the t-plane.

problem also applies to the case of the air-gap of a dynamo which
changes suddenly in length from c to g. The solution will be
given for the case where the strip is infinitely long and it will
be seen by inspection of Fig. 46 that it is correct for all practical
purposes if the length of the strip is 3 or 4 times c.

It is convenient to take the origin in the z-plane at the corner
where the decrease in section from c to g occurs (see Fig. 43).

The z-plane and the corresponding *t*-plane are shown in Figs. 43 and 44. The point $t = 0$ is taken at the convergence of the lines *LM* and *PN* at an infinite distance to the left on the z-plane, and the origin in the z-plane corresponds to $t = 1$. We find that this choice simplifies the algebra considerably. *R* corresponds to $t = a$, the value of *a* to be determined later.

The angles inside the figure in the z-plane at *P* and *R* depend on whether *c* is greater or less than *g*. We have taken *c* greater than *g* so that we have three right angles at *P* and one right angle at *R*. The expression for the transformation will only hold for the case $c/g > 1$.

t – Plane

| L | | MN | | P | R | | S |
| -∞ | | 0 | | 1 | a | | + ∞ |

FIG. 44. The *t*-plane, showing the horizontal line to which Fig. 43 has been opened out.

The Schwarzian equation is

$$\frac{dz}{dt} = A(t-0)^{(0/\pi)-1}(t-1)^{(\beta/\pi)-1}(t-a)^{(\alpha/\pi)-1}.$$

At *MN*, $t = 0$, internal angle $= 0$, $\dfrac{0}{\pi} - 1 = -1$;

at *P*, $t = 1$, „ $= \dfrac{3\pi}{2}$, $\dfrac{3}{2} - 1 = \dfrac{1}{2}$;

at *R*, $t = a$, „ $= \dfrac{\pi}{2}$, $\dfrac{1}{2} - 1 = -\dfrac{1}{2}$.

So we have

$$\frac{dz}{dt} = At^{-1} \times (t-1)^{\frac{1}{2}} \times (t-a)^{-\frac{1}{2}} = \frac{A}{t}\sqrt{\frac{t-1}{t-a}}.$$

At a point near $t = 0$ let $t = re^{j\theta}$; $dt = jre^{j\theta}\,d\theta = jt\,d\theta$,

$$dz = jA\sqrt{\frac{t-1}{t-a}}\,d\theta,$$

and, since *t* is small as compared with 1 and *a*,

$$\sqrt{\frac{t-1}{t-a}} = \frac{1}{\sqrt{a}}.$$

$$\int_0^{jg} dz = \frac{jA}{\sqrt{a}} \int_0^{\pi} d\theta, \qquad \therefore \quad jg = j\frac{A\pi}{\sqrt{a}}.$$

$$\therefore \quad a = \frac{A^2\pi^2}{g^2}.$$

Now integrate over an infinitely large semicircle of large radius R taking $t = R\epsilon^{j\theta}$, $dt = jt\, d\theta$.

Since t is large as compared with 1 and a,

$$\sqrt{\frac{t-1}{t-a}} = 1.$$

$$\int_{j(g-c)}^{jg} dz = jA \int_0^{\pi} d\theta.$$

$$jc = j\pi A, \qquad \therefore \quad A = \frac{c}{\pi}.$$

$$a = \frac{c^2}{g^2}, \qquad \therefore \quad a \text{ is greater than } 1.$$

Thus we get

$$\frac{dz}{dt} = \frac{c}{\pi t}\sqrt{\frac{t-1}{t-a}}.$$

Write $a = b^2$, then

$$z = \frac{c}{\pi}\int \frac{1}{t}\sqrt{\frac{t-1}{t-b^2}}\, dt = \frac{c}{\pi}\int \frac{t-1}{t}\,\frac{1}{\sqrt{(t-b^2)(t-1)}}\, dt$$

$$= \frac{c}{\pi}\int \frac{dt}{\sqrt{(t-b^2)(t-1)}} - \frac{dt}{t\sqrt{(t-b^2)(t-1)}}.$$

Taking the first expression under the integral sign,

$$\frac{dt}{\sqrt{t^2-(b^2+1)t+b^2}} = \frac{2dt}{\sqrt{4t^2-4(b^2+1)t+4b^2}}$$

$$= \frac{2dt}{\sqrt{\{2t-(b^2+1)\}^2-(b^2-1)^2}}.$$

This is like the standard form

$$\int \frac{du}{u^2-a^2} = \cosh^{-1}\frac{u}{a}.$$

$$\therefore \quad \int \frac{dt}{\sqrt{(t-b^2)(t-1)}} = \cosh^{-1}\frac{2t-(b^2+1)}{b^2-1}.$$

Taking now the second expression,

$$\frac{dt}{t\sqrt{(t-b^2)(t-1)}} = \frac{dt}{t\sqrt{t^2-(b^2+1)t+b^2}}$$

$$= \frac{dt}{t^2\sqrt{1-\dfrac{(b^2+1)}{t}+\dfrac{b^2}{t^2}}}.$$

Let $v = \dfrac{1}{t}$, $\therefore$ $dv = -\dfrac{dt}{t^2}$.

$$\frac{-dv}{\sqrt{1-(b^2+1)v+b^2v^2}} = \frac{-2\,dv}{\sqrt{4-4(b^2+1)v+4b^2v^2}}$$

$$= \frac{-2\,dv}{\sqrt{\left\{\dfrac{b^2+1}{b}-2bv\right\}^2-\left\{\left(\dfrac{b^2+1}{b}\right)^2-4\right\}}} = \frac{-2\,dv}{\sqrt{\left\{\dfrac{b^2+1}{b}-2bv\right\}^2-\left(\dfrac{b^2-1}{b}\right)^2}}.$$

Write $u = \dfrac{b^2+1}{b}-2bv$, $\therefore$ $du = -2b\,dv$.

The second integral $= \dfrac{1}{b}\displaystyle\int \dfrac{du}{\sqrt{u^2-\left\{\dfrac{b^2-1}{b}\right\}^2}} = \dfrac{1}{b}\cosh^{-1}\dfrac{bu}{b^2-1}$.

Substituting $v = 1/t$,

$$u = \frac{b^2+1}{b}-\frac{2b}{t} = \frac{(b^2+1)t-2b^2}{bt}.$$

Collecting the two integrals and substituting a for b^2 and adding a complex constant,

$$z = \frac{c}{\pi}\left\{\cosh^{-1}\frac{2t-(a+1)}{a-1}-\frac{1}{\sqrt{a}}\cosh^{-1}\frac{(a+1)t-2a}{(a-1)t}\right\}+D+jE.$$

We will now evaluate the complex constant $D+jE$ on the assumed conditions

$$z = 0; \qquad w = 0; \qquad t = 1.$$

The w-plane is the plane in which we have a parallel distribution of stream-lines as in Fig. 45, so that $w = V+jC$.

$$0 = \frac{c}{\pi}\left\{\cosh^{-1}\frac{2-a-1}{a-1}-\frac{1}{\sqrt{a}}\cosh^{-1}\frac{a+1-2a}{a-1}\right\}+D+jE$$

$$= \frac{c}{\pi} \left\{ \cosh^{-1} \frac{\text{I}-a}{a-\text{I}} - \frac{\text{I}}{\sqrt{a}} \cosh^{-1} \frac{\text{I}-a}{a-\text{I}} \right\} + D + jE$$

$$= \frac{c}{\pi} \left\{ \left(\text{I} - \frac{\text{I}}{\sqrt{a}} \right) \cosh^{-1}(-\text{I}) \right\} + D + jE.$$

We have now to investigate the meaning of $\cosh^{-1}(-\text{I})$.

Let $\cosh^{-1}(-\text{I}) = p + jq$, p and q being real.

$$\cosh(p+jq) = -\text{I},$$

$$\tfrac{1}{2}\{\epsilon^{(p+jq)} + \epsilon^{-(p+jq)}\} = -\text{I},$$

$$\tfrac{1}{2}\epsilon^{p}(\cos q + j \sin q) + \tfrac{1}{2}\epsilon^{-p}(\cos q - j \sin q) = -\text{I},$$

$$\tfrac{1}{2}(\epsilon^{p} + \epsilon^{-p})\cos q + \tfrac{1}{2}j(\epsilon^{p} - \epsilon^{-p})\sin q = -\text{I}.$$

Equating real and imaginary terms,

$$\cosh p \cos q = -\text{I}, \qquad \sinh p \sin q = 0.$$

$$\therefore \quad \text{either } p \text{ or } \sin q = 0.$$

If $p = 0$, $\cosh p = \text{I}$,

$$\cos q = -\text{I} \quad \text{and} \quad q = \pi.$$

If $\sin q = 0$, $\qquad\qquad \cos q = \text{I}$ or $-\text{I}$.

It is impossible that $\cosh p = -\text{I}$ because p is real. Therefore $\cos q$ must be $-\text{I}$ and $q = \pi$.

Thus we have

$$p = 0 \quad \text{and} \quad q = \pi$$

$$\cosh^{-1}(-\text{I}) = j\pi.$$

Returning to substitute this result

$$0 = \frac{c}{\pi} \left(\text{I} - \frac{\text{I}}{\sqrt{a}} \right) j\pi + D + jE.$$

Equating real and imaginary terms

$$D = 0 \qquad E = -c \left(\text{I} - \frac{\text{I}}{\sqrt{a}} \right).$$

We have now to put into the t-plane a stream-function with a source at $t = 0$ (MN on Fig. 43) there being a stream-line along NS and another along ML. This is done as explained on p. 35 by putting a parallel flow in the w-plane so that

$$w = V + jC.$$

In Fig. 45 the line $N'S'$ is taken as the stream-line $C = 0$ and

I

$M'L'$ as the stream-line $C = I$. The total current in the strip is I. The w-plane is then opened out by folding back the line $M'L'$ through the angle π. This transforms the w-plane into the t-plane. As explained on p. 35 the Schwarzian transformation in this case gives us the relation

$$w = \frac{I}{\pi}\log t + \text{const.}$$

and if we take $t = 1$ when $w = 0$ the constant is eliminated.

Thus
$$t = \epsilon^{\frac{\pi}{I}w}.$$

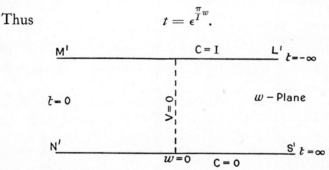

Fig. 45. The w-plane containing a parallel distribution of current $w = V + jC$.

Writing $\dfrac{\pi}{I} = k$ for ease in type setting,

$$t = \epsilon^{kw}.$$

The complete solution then is

$$z = \frac{c}{\pi}\left\{\cosh^{-1}\frac{2\epsilon^{kw}-(a+1)}{a-1} - \frac{1}{\sqrt{a}}\cosh^{-1}\frac{(a+1)\epsilon^{kw}-2a}{(a-1)\epsilon^{kw}} - j\pi\left(1-\frac{1}{\sqrt{a}}\right)\right\}$$

where $k = \dfrac{\pi}{I}$ and $a = \dfrac{c^2}{g^2}$. I is the value of the total current in the strip.

When we come to make a plot of the stream-lines and equipotential lines the following points should be noted with regard to the scales to be adopted. The scale of the figure in the z-plane (see Fig. 46) is derived from the constant c. For instance if the dimension c of the strip in Fig. 43 is 10 cm. wide and our paper is not large enough to draw it full size we can adopt a half scale so that 0·5 cm. of our figure represents 1 cm. of the strip. This does not in any way affect the shape of the stream-line. The ratio of c to g is looked after in the formula by the constant a. The electrical conditions are introduced into the formula by the term $\epsilon^{\frac{\pi}{I}w}$, and it does not matter to what scale the w-figure may have been drawn. As $w = 0$ corresponds to $z = 0$, the zero stream-line passes through $z = 0$ and the stream-line of value I corresponds with the top line of the z-figure. This is because we made jg correspond with jI. The position of the equipotential lines will come out from the formula on the assumption that resistance between opposite sides of a square centimetre of the strip is 1 ohm. Let r be the actual resistance between opposite sides of this square; then all the voltages are multiplied by r. Suppose for instance that $r = 3$. Then we should plot the equipotential lines as given by the formula, but label the line that is at 1 volt (by the formula) '3 volts' and so with all the other equipotential lines. The shapes are not altered but the labels are altered. It is as though the variation of the resistance altered the unit by which we measured the electric pressure. Indeed, if this were not so, the function $V+jC$ would not comply with the conditions imposed on p. 15. It is by altering the units in which V is measured that we make it comply.

In order to illustrate the process of plotting the stream-lines and equipotential lines in any particular case, Mr. S. M. Taylor has prepared Fig. 46 which shows the values calculated from the above formula when $c = 2g$. He has taken $I = 1$ ampere. In his original figure the dimension c of the strip was 2 cm. and the calculations are based on that value, but in Fig. 46 the width c has been made 5 cm. and g has been made 2·5 cm. so as to get the curves on a larger scale.

The calculations are made on the simpler data. The stream function C has the value $I = 1$ ampere at the point where $z = jg$ and $g = 1$, so that

$$C_1 = I = 1;\ g = 1;\ c = 2;\ a = 4;\ \sqrt{a} = 2.$$

Now $$w = V+jC, \qquad \frac{\pi}{C_1}w = \pi(V+jC).$$

$$\epsilon^{kw} = \epsilon^{\pi(V+jC)} = \epsilon^{\pi V}\epsilon^{j\pi C} = \epsilon^{\pi V}(\cos C\pi + j\sin C\pi).$$

For example, for various values of the stream function C, when

$$C = 0 \qquad\qquad \epsilon^{j\pi C} = 1 + j\,0$$
$$= 0{\cdot}25 \qquad\qquad = 0{\cdot}707 + j\,0{\cdot}707$$
$$= 0{\cdot}5 \qquad\qquad = 0 + j\,1$$
$$= 0{\cdot}75 \qquad\qquad = -0{\cdot}707 + j\,0{\cdot}707$$
$$= 1 \qquad\qquad = -1 + j\,0.$$

The expression to be evaluated is now

$$z = \frac{2}{\pi}\left\{\cosh^{-1}\left[\frac{2\epsilon^{\pi V}}{3}(\cos C\pi + j\sin C\pi) - \frac{5}{3}\right] - \right.$$
$$\left. - \tfrac{1}{2}\cosh^{-1}\left[\frac{5}{3} - \frac{8}{3\epsilon^{\pi V}}(\cos C\pi - j\sin C\pi)\right] - j\tfrac{1}{2}\pi\right\}.$$

The change in sign in the second term occurs because

$$\frac{1}{\epsilon^{\pi w}} = \frac{1}{\epsilon^{\pi(V+jC)}} = \frac{1}{\epsilon^{\pi V}} \times \epsilon^{-j\pi C} = \frac{1}{\epsilon^{\pi V}}(\cos C\pi - j\sin C\pi).$$

The values of the hyperbolic cosines can be obtained from Kennelly's *Tables of Complex Hyperbolic and Circular Functions*. In using these tables it should be noted that the values are given in terms of $x + jq$ instead of $x + jy$ where $q = 2y/\pi$ (see p. 50).

It will in general be necessary to interpolate between two values given in the tables to get a higher degree of accuracy. The interpolations differ slightly from the examples shown in Kennelly's *Tables* because we are dealing with inverse quantities.

The following example of the evaluation of the formula for $V = 0$ and $C = 0{\cdot}5$ illustrates the method of interpolation:

$$\epsilon^{\pi V} = 1 \qquad \cos C\pi = 0 \qquad \sin C\pi = 1.$$

$$z = \frac{2}{\pi}\{\cosh^{-1}(-1{\cdot}667 + j\,0{\cdot}667) -$$
$$- \tfrac{1}{2}\cosh^{-1}(1{\cdot}667 + j\,2{\cdot}667) - j\,1{\cdot}5708\}.$$

To evaluate $\cosh^{-1}(-1{\cdot}667 + j\,0{\cdot}667)$. From the tables for $\cosh(x+jq)$ find

$$\cosh(1{\cdot}2 + j\,1{\cdot}75) = -1{\cdot}67283 + j\,0{\cdot}57765$$
$$\underline{\cosh(1{\cdot}2 + j\,1{\cdot}7) = -1{\cdot}61331 + j\,0{\cdot}68528}$$
$$\text{diff. for } j\,0{\cdot}05 = -0{\cdot}05952 - j\,0{\cdot}10763$$
$$\underline{\text{diff. for } j\,0{\cdot}045 = -0{\cdot}05369 - j\,0{\cdot}097}$$
$$\cosh(1{\cdot}2 + j\,1{\cdot}745) = -1{\cdot}667 + j\,0{\cdot}58828$$

$$\cosh(1{\cdot}25+j\ 1{\cdot}7) = -1{\cdot}68260+j\ 0{\cdot}72726$$
$$\cosh(1{\cdot}25+j\ 1{\cdot}65) = -1{\cdot}61014+j\ 0{\cdot}83700$$

diff. for $j\ 0{\cdot}05\qquad = -0{\cdot}07246-j\ 0{\cdot}10974$
diff. for $j\ 0{\cdot}03925 = -0{\cdot}05686-j\ 0{\cdot}0862$

$$\cosh(1{\cdot}25+j\ 1{\cdot}68925) = -1{\cdot}667+j\ 0{\cdot}75080$$
$$\cosh(1{\cdot}2+j\ 1{\cdot}745)\quad = -1{\cdot}667+j\ 0{\cdot}58828$$

$0{\cdot}05-j\ 0{\cdot}5575\qquad =$ diff. for $j\ 0{\cdot}16252$
$0{\cdot}0242-j\ 0{\cdot}027\quad =$ diff. for $j\ 0{\cdot}07872$

$$\cosh(1{\cdot}2242+j\ 1{\cdot}718) = -1{\cdot}667+j\ 0{\cdot}667$$

Since $q = 1{\cdot}718$, $\qquad \frac{1}{2}\pi q = 2{\cdot}7$ radians.

$\therefore\quad \cosh^{-1}(-1{\cdot}667+j\ 0{\cdot}667) = 1{\cdot}2242+j\ 2{\cdot}700.$

To evaluate $\cosh^{-1}(1{\cdot}667+j\ 2{\cdot}667)$

$$\cosh(1{\cdot}85+j\ 0{\cdot}7)\ =\quad 1{\cdot}47934+j\ 2{\cdot}76327$$
$$\cosh(1{\cdot}85+j\ 0{\cdot}65) =\quad 1{\cdot}70258+j\ 2{\cdot}64429$$

diff. for $j\ 0{\cdot}05\qquad = -0{\cdot}22324+j\ 0{\cdot}11898$
diff. for $j\ 0{\cdot}00798 = -0{\cdot}03558+j\ 0{\cdot}01895$

$$\cosh(1{\cdot}85+j\ 0{\cdot}65798) = 1{\cdot}667+j\ 2{\cdot}66324$$

$$\cosh(1{\cdot}9+j\ 0{\cdot}7)\ = 1{\cdot}55162+j\ 2{\cdot}91196$$
$$\cosh(1{\cdot}9+j\ 0{\cdot}65) = 1{\cdot}78576+j\ 2{\cdot}78657$$

diff. for $j\ 0{\cdot}05\qquad = -0{\cdot}23414+j\ 0{\cdot}12539$
diff. for $j\ 0{\cdot}0254 = -0{\cdot}11876+j\ 0{\cdot}06360$

$$\cosh(1{\cdot}9+j\ 0{\cdot}67540)\quad = 1{\cdot}667+j\ 2{\cdot}85017$$
$$\cosh(1{\cdot}85+j\ 0{\cdot}65798) = 1{\cdot}667+j\ 2{\cdot}66324$$

$0{\cdot}05+j\ 0{\cdot}01742\qquad =$ diff. for $j\ 0{\cdot}18693$
$0{\cdot}0101+j\ 0{\cdot}00035\ =$ diff. for $j\ 0{\cdot}00376$

$$\cosh(1{\cdot}8601+j\ 0{\cdot}65833) = 1{\cdot}667+j\ 2{\cdot}667$$
$$q = 0{\cdot}65833,\ \tfrac{1}{2}\pi q = 1{\cdot}035\ \text{radians.}$$

$\therefore\quad \cosh^{-1}(1{\cdot}667+j\ 2{\cdot}667) = 1{\cdot}8601+j\ 1{\cdot}035.$

$$z = \frac{2}{\pi}\{1{\cdot}2242+j\ 2{\cdot}700-0{\cdot}93-j\ 0{\cdot}5175-j\ 1{\cdot}5708\}$$

$$= \frac{2}{\pi}\{0{\cdot}2942+j\ 0{\cdot}6117\}$$

$$= 0{\cdot}187+j\ 0{\cdot}389 = x+jy.$$

This value is transferred to the table of values given on p. 63 and the values have been plotted on Fig. 46.

It is interesting to watch the imaginary term when $C = 1$ and when $C = 0$.

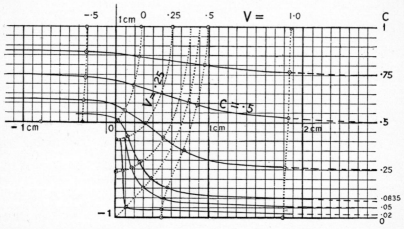

FIG. 46. Stream-lines and equipotential lines in a conducting strip which is 2 cm. wide along half its length and 1 cm. wide along the other half. The change in width is made by the right-angled corners shown in the figure. Scale 2·5 cm. = 1 cm.

When $C = 1$, $\qquad e^{j\pi C} = -1 + j\,0,$

so the expression for z takes the form

$$z = \frac{2}{\pi}\left\{\cosh^{-1}(-m+j\,0)-\tfrac{1}{2}\cosh^{-1}(+n-j\,0)-j\frac{\pi}{2}\right\},$$

where m and n are numbers depending on the value of V.

Taking the first term we have seen by the argument on p. 57 that whenever the real term (such as $-m$) is negative, the unreal part of $\cosh^{-1}(-m+j\,0)$ must be equal to $j\pi$ in order to introduce the minus sign by the multiplier $\cos\pi$. Further, whenever the real term (such as $+n$) is positive, the unreal part of $\cosh^{-1}(n-j\,0)$ must be equal to zero. Therefore, we have the unreal part of z:

$$jy = \frac{2}{\pi}\left\{+j\pi-j\,0-j\frac{\pi}{2}\right\} = \frac{2}{\pi}\left\{j\frac{\pi}{2}\right\} = j\,1\cdot0.$$

As a consequence, for $C = 1$, whatever be the value of V, the stream function follows the line $y = 1$. This is of course obvious

TABLE OF VALUES OF z FOR CURVES

$V \rightarrow$ / $C \downarrow$	−0·5	0	0·25	0·375	0·44	0·5	1·0
0	−0·368	0	−j0·177	−j0·512	−j1·0	0·483−j1·0	1·79−j1·0
0·02	..	..	..	0·0695−j0·507	0·104−j0·885	0·489−j0·91	..
0·05	..	..	..	0·162−j0·478	0·298−j0·678	0·52−j0·80	..
0·0835	..	0·0222+j0·025	0·354+j0·464	0·248−j0·418	0·381−j0·587	0·562−j0·68	..
0·25	−0·353+j0·232	0·0938+j0·129	0·32−j0·0005	0·505−j0·159	..	0·735−j0·285	1·81−j0·468
0·5	−0·331+j0·475	0·187+j0·389	..	..	..	0·88+j0·185	1·85+j0·055
0·75	−0·315+j0·73	0·249+j0·69	..	..	..	0·95+j0·607	1·86+j0·529
1·0	−0·309+j1·0	0·268+j1·0	0·620+j1·0	..	..	0·985+j1·0	1·875+j1·0

from the shape of the strip, but it is interesting to see how so complicated a function gives such a simple result.

For $C = 0$, $\qquad\qquad \epsilon^{j\pi C} = 1 + j\,0$.

Where V is negative, $\left(\dfrac{2\epsilon^{\pi V}}{3} - \dfrac{5}{3}\right)$ is always negative and $\left(\dfrac{5}{3} - \dfrac{8}{3\epsilon^{\pi V}}\right)$ is always negative, so that the terms take the form

$$\frac{2}{\pi}\{\cosh^{-1}(-m+j\,0)-\tfrac{1}{2}\cosh^{-1}(-n-j\,0)-j\tfrac{1}{2}\pi\},$$

and by the arguments on p. 57,

$$jy = j\pi - j\tfrac{1}{2}\pi - j\tfrac{1}{2}\pi = 0.$$

Thus the stream-line for negative values of V follows the horizontal line through zero.

For positive values of V greater than 0·44, both $\left(\dfrac{2\epsilon^{\pi V}}{3} - \dfrac{5}{3}\right)$ and $\left(\dfrac{5}{3} - \dfrac{8}{3\epsilon^{\pi V}}\right)$ are positive, so that both the unreal parts of the $\cosh^{-1}$ terms come out zero and we have left

$$jy = \frac{2}{\pi}\{-j\tfrac{1}{2}\pi\} = -j.$$

For these positive values of V the stream-line follows the horizontal line $y = -1$.

In addition, there are further sets of cases, when the equipotential lines end on the y-axis between 0 and -1. Thus, for $V = 0\cdot375$ and $C = 0$,

$$z = \frac{2}{\pi}\left\{\cosh^{-1}(0\cdot498)-\tfrac{1}{2}\cosh^{-1}(0\cdot846)-j\frac{\pi}{2}\right\}.$$

Now $\cosh^{-1}u$ has no real solution when $u < 1$ but

$$\cosh^{-1}u = j\cos^{-1}u.$$

$$\therefore \quad 2z = \frac{2}{\pi}\left\{j\cos^{-1}(0\cdot498)-\tfrac{1}{2}j\cos^{-1}(0\cdot846)-j\frac{\pi}{2}\right\}.$$

The angles are, of course, expressed in radians,

$$\therefore \quad z = \frac{2}{\pi}\left\{j\,1\cdot05-j\,0\cdot2825-j\frac{\pi}{2}\right\} = -j\,0\cdot512.$$

At the origin $V = 0$. To find V at the other corner, we do not use the z, w equation, which is complicated, but the simpler relation between t and w.

We know that at this corner $t = a$.

$$\therefore \quad w = \frac{I}{\pi}\log a \quad \text{and} \quad I = 1,$$

$$a = \frac{c^2}{g^2} = 4,$$

$$\therefore \quad w = V + jC = \frac{1}{\pi}\log_e 4 = 0.44,$$

$$\therefore \quad V = 0.44.$$

Therefore, by plotting for $V = 0.44$ and a few other values of C, we have the equipotential line which terminates at this corner.

This problem is analogous to the problem of finding the distribution of magnetic flux in the air-gap of a dynamo at a place where the length of the gap is suddenly increased to a length just slightly greater than the normal length. Such a place sometimes occurs where room is left for a band of steel wire and the wire does not entirely fill the space. In case the width of the band is great as compared with the length of the gap, the solution given in this example is applicable with a great degree of approximation.

Fig. 46 is applicable but we must take the full lines to represent lines of equi-magnetic potential and the dotted lines to represent lines of magnetic flux.

K

EXAMPLE NO. 7

ELECTRIC CONDUCTOR IN AIR-GAP

INVESTIGATION OF THE MAGNETIC FIELD MADE BY A STRAIGHT
CONDUCTOR CARRYING AN ELECTRIC CURRENT PLACED MIDWAY
BETWEEN TWO PARALLEL INFINITE SURFACES OF PERMEABLE
MATERIAL: FOR EXAMPLE, A STRAIGHT CONDUCTOR IN THE AIR-
GAP OF A DYNAMO.

LET the distance between the surfaces of permeable material
be g and let the current of I' absolute units be flowing in
the conductor downwards through the plane of the paper in

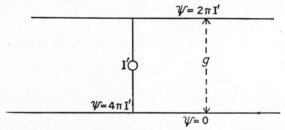

FIG. 47. Two surfaces of permeable material (like the air-gap of a dynamo)
with a conductor half-way between them carrying the current I' absolute units.

Fig. 47. Then the change in magnetic potential as we go once
round the conductor is $4\pi I'$ (see p. 7). In going half-way
round it is $2\pi I'$. Let us arbitrarily take the magnetic potential of
the lower surface in Fig. 47 at $\psi = 0$. The work done in carrying
a unit pole against the magnetic field from the lower surface across
the gap g on the right of the conductor up to the other surface
will be $2\pi I'$ ergs. If we now go to the left of the conductor and
bring the unit pole downwards we shall still be working against
the force in the magnetic field and the work done will be another
$2\pi I'$ making the total work done $4\pi I'$. Thus it is impossible to
ascribe any definite potential to either of the surfaces and the inter-
vening space unless we confine our movements of the magnetic
pole by a certain barrier (see p. 6).

Draw a vertical line through the conductor as in Fig. 47 and
restrict our movements to points to the right of this barrier.
Then all points on this line can be given a definite potential.

The vertical line downwards below the conductor and the lower permeable surface may be taken as $\psi = 0$, and the line above the conductor and the upper permeable surface will then be at the potential $\psi = 2\pi I'$.

The case is analogous to the distribution of stream-lines in a strip of metal having parallel edges and of width g, where an electric current is fed in at both ends and taken out at a point S (see Fig. 48). If we were to take a strip of metal like that described on p. 3, of width g, and feed in an electric current of $2\pi I$ amperes* at each end and take it out at the point S, the lines of

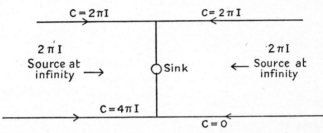

Fig. 48. Showing how the magnetic problem can be converted into an electric problem. A strip of metal of the same width as the air-gap carries electric currents fed from each end to a sink having the same position as I' in Fig. 47. If the current from each end of the strip has a value of $2\pi I$ amperes, the value of the stream function C is the same as the value of the magnetic potential in the case depicted in Fig. 47, and if the strip has the resistance described in the text the equipotential lines in the electric case correspond to the lines of magnetic flux in the magnetic case.

flow of current in this case would be the same as the lines of equimagnetic potential in the case considered in Fig. 47. The stream function may be taken arbitrarily at $C = 0$ on the bottom edge of the strip, and as we cross the strip on the right of the sink, we cross the total current $2\pi I$. If we then pass to the left of the source and pass downwards to the lower edge, we cross another current $2\pi I$. The lines of equipotential in the metal strip will be the same shape as the magnetic lines in the case taken in Fig. 47.

We will first take the current case and afterwards use the

---

* Note the current is now measured in amperes. This is because we want to make the expression for the upper line the same in both cases. The strip has a resistance of 1 ohm for 1 sq. cm., so 1 ampere per cm. width gives a drop of 1 volt per cm.

solution for the magnetic case. If we cut the strip through the vertical line shown in Fig. 48 and feed in a current of $2\pi I$ at a great distance to the right, the current distribution in the half strip will be exactly the same as before.

To get the equations for the lines of flow, we begin by putting in the z-plane (Fig. 49) a rectilinear figure having the same shape as the edges of the metal strip in Fig. 48.

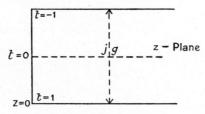

FIG. 49. The z-plane corresponding to one half of Fig. 48.

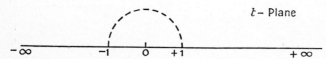

FIG. 50. The t-plane to which the lines in Fig. 49 have been opened out.

To straighten out this figure into the straight line in the t-plane, we have $t = \cosh\dfrac{\pi z}{g}$ (see p. 48).

We have seen on p. 48 that the constant of integration is eliminated by making the point $z = 0$ correspond with the point $t = 1$ in the t-plane.

In Fig. 49 the origin in the z-plane is taken at the left-hand bottom corner and corresponds to $t = 1$. Now it is convenient, for the purposes of symmetry, to have the origin in the z-plane at the sink S. That is we wish to move the origin to the point that corresponds to $t = 0$. We must, therefore, add $jg/2$ to z. Then for the diagram shown in Fig. 51 the transformation gives us

$$t = \cosh\left(\frac{\pi}{g}z + j\frac{\pi}{2}\right) = j\sinh\frac{\pi}{g}z.$$

Now put an electric sink at the point $t = 0$ in the t-plane. We have seen on p. 36 that a sink at the origin in the t-plane gives a distribution of the potential function V, and the stream function C, such that

$$V+jC = K\log t + \text{const.}$$

Therefore, if we fold up the straight line of the t-plane so as to make the edge stream-lines follow the right-angled shape shown in Fig. 51 the distribution of potential and stream function will be

$$V+jC = K\log j\sinh\frac{\pi}{g}z + \text{complex constant}$$

$$= K\log\sinh\frac{\pi}{g}(x+jy) + K\log j + \text{const.}$$

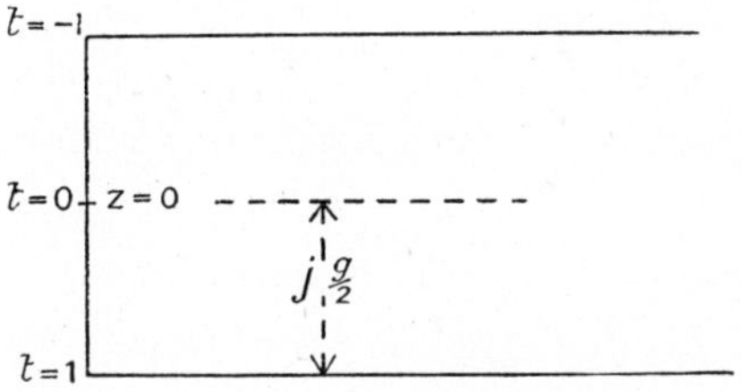

$t=-1$

$t=0$ $z=0$

$j.\frac{g}{2}$

$t=1$

FIG. 51. Showing the effect of shifting the zero in the z-plane.

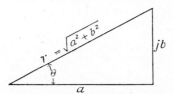

FIG. 52. Showing how $a+jb$ is converted into $re^{j\theta}$.

Since $j = \epsilon^{\frac{1}{2}j\pi}$, $\qquad \log j = \frac{1}{2}j\pi$.

The value of the constant of integration will depend finally upon the position that we take for the stream-line $C = 0$. We shall for the moment leave it out (together with the $\frac{1}{2}jK\pi$) and bring it in later when we are in a position to evaluate it.

Let us write $\pi/g = c$ and investigate further the expression

$$\log\sinh cz = \log\sinh(cx+jcy)$$

$$= \log(\sinh cx\cos cy + j\cosh cx\sin cy)$$

$$= \log(\qquad a \qquad + \qquad jb \qquad), \text{ say.}$$

Let the real term in the brackets be the length of a horizontal line $(= a)$ in Fig. 52 and the unreal term that of a vertical line $(= jb)$.

Then the hypotenuse $\sqrt{a^2+b^2}$ is the radius r when the expression in the brackets is put in the form $re^{j\theta}$.

$$\log re^{j\theta} = \log r + j\theta,$$

$$\log r = \log \sqrt{a^2+b^2} = \tfrac{1}{2}\log(a^2+b^2)$$
$$= \tfrac{1}{2}\log(\sinh^2 cx \cos^2 cy + \cosh^2 cx \sin^2 cy),$$

and $\tan\theta = b/a$.

Now
$$\sinh^2 cx = \tfrac{1}{2}(\cosh 2cx - 1),$$
$$\cos^2 cy = \tfrac{1}{2}(1 + \cos 2cy),$$
$$\cosh^2 cx = \tfrac{1}{2}(\cosh 2cx + 1),$$
$$\sin^2 cy = \tfrac{1}{2}(1 - \cos 2cy).$$
$$\therefore \quad a^2+b^2 = \tfrac{1}{2}(\cosh 2cx - \cos 2cy).$$

$$\log r = \tfrac{1}{2}\log \tfrac{1}{2}\left(\cosh \frac{2\pi}{g}x - \cos \frac{2\pi}{g}y\right),$$

$$\theta = \arctan \frac{\cosh \dfrac{\pi}{g}x \sin \dfrac{\pi}{g}y}{\sinh \dfrac{\pi}{g}x \cos \dfrac{\pi}{g}y} = \arctan \frac{\tan \dfrac{\pi}{g}y}{\tanh \dfrac{\pi}{g}x}.$$

$$V+jC = K\tfrac{1}{2}\log \tfrac{1}{2}\left(\cosh \frac{2\pi}{g}x - \cos \frac{2\pi}{g}y\right) + jK\arctan \frac{\tan \dfrac{\pi y}{g}}{\tanh \dfrac{\pi x}{g}} +$$

$$+ A + jB + \tfrac{1}{2}jK\pi.$$

Let $C = 0$ when $x =$ any positive value to infinity and $y = -g/2$. Taking x at infinity we have

$$jK\arctan \frac{\tan(-\tfrac{1}{2}\pi)}{1} = -\tfrac{1}{2}jK\pi,$$

$$0 = -\tfrac{1}{2}jK\pi + jB + \tfrac{1}{2}jK\pi. \qquad \therefore \quad B = 0.$$

Again let $C = 2\pi I$ when $x = \infty$ and $y = +g/2$,

$$jK\arctan \frac{\tan \tfrac{1}{2}\pi}{1} = \tfrac{1}{2}jK\pi,$$

$$j\,2\pi I = j\,2K\tfrac{1}{2}\pi. \qquad \therefore \quad 2I = K.$$

To evaluate A,

$$V = I\log \tfrac{1}{2}\left(\cosh \frac{2\pi x}{g} - \cos \frac{2\pi y}{g}\right) + A.$$

Let $V = 0$ when $x = 0$ and $y = -g/2$ (see Fig. 53).

$$\cosh\frac{2\pi x}{g} = 1 \quad \text{and} \quad \cos(-\pi) = -1,$$

$$0 = I\log 1 + A, \qquad \therefore \quad A = 0.$$

$$V+jC = I\log\tfrac{1}{2}\left(\cosh\frac{2\pi x}{g} - \cos\frac{2\pi y}{g}\right) + j2I\arctan\frac{\tan\dfrac{\pi y}{g}}{\tanh\dfrac{\pi x}{g}} + jI\pi.$$

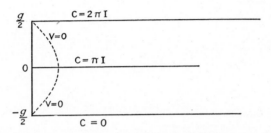

FIG. 53. For evaluating the constant K.

This is the solution for the electrical case when the total current $2\pi I$ amperes is fed into the strip and taken out at the sink S (Fig. 48).

Now return to the magnetic problem. As we have seen on p. 7, a current of I' absolute units passing in a wire at right angles to the paper (Fig. 47) makes a difference of magnetic potential of $2\pi I'$ units between the two surfaces of high permeability. When we consider the region to the right of the wire and take the potential of the lower surface as zero ($\psi = 0$), the magnetic potential of the upper surface is $\psi = 2\pi I'$.

The lines of equipotential in the magnetic case are the same as the lines of equal stream function in the electric case considered above; and the lines of constant flux ϕ are the same as the lines of constant electric potential in the electric case.

Thus we have for $\phi + j\psi$ exactly the same expression as we have for $V+jC$, except that we substitute I' absolute units of current for I amperes.

If we wish to measure the current in the wire, in the magnetic case, in amperes then the solution is

$$\phi + j\psi = 0 \cdot 1 I \log \tfrac{1}{2}\left(\cosh\frac{2\pi x}{g} - \cos\frac{2\pi y}{g}\right) +$$

$$+ j\, 0 \cdot 2 I \arctan \frac{\tan\dfrac{\pi y}{g}}{\tanh\dfrac{\pi x}{g}} + j\, 0 \cdot 1 I \pi.$$

We can get rid of the constant term $j\, 0 \cdot 1 I\pi$ by taking the surface mid-way between the two permeable surfaces at the potential o (instead of the lower permeable surface). The result then comes

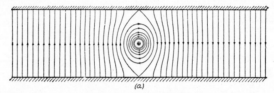

(a)

FIG. 54. The magnetic lines across an air-gap carrying a current along the conductor described in Fig. 47.

(Reproduced from Hague, *Electromagnetic Problems in Electrical Engineering.*)

out in the same form* as that given by Hague on p. 167 of his book. Fig. 54, reproduced from his book, shows how the magnetic lines ($\phi = $ constant) are shaped.

* The coefficient $\tfrac{1}{2}$ in the first term will become unity (as in Hague's formula) if we take the line of zero flux at $x = 0$, $y = g/4$. This is seen by the following:

$$\log\tfrac{1}{2}\left(\cosh\frac{2\pi x}{g} - \cos\frac{2\pi y}{g}\right) + A = \log\left(\cosh\frac{2\pi x}{g} - \cos\frac{2\pi y}{g}\right) - \log 2 + A.$$

Let $\phi = 0$ when $x = 0$ and $y = g/4$.

$$\cos\tfrac{1}{2}\pi = 0,$$

$$0 = \log(1 - 0) - \log 2 + A.$$

∴ $A = \log 2$, and this cancels out with the $-\log 2$ arising from the coefficient $\tfrac{1}{2}$.

EXAMPLE NO. 8

THE FRINGING FLUX BETWEEN TWO POLES OF A DYNAMO

THIS method has been used by F. W. Carter to calculate the strength of the magnetic field between two poles of a dynamo and to find the total amount of fringing flux. The simplest case is where we assume that the poles are rectangular in shape and that the diameter of the armature of the dynamo is so great that the surface of the armature may be taken as substantially flat. The arrangement is then as shown in Fig. 55.

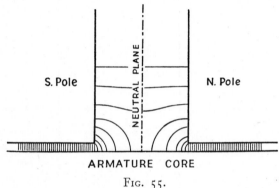

S. Pole   NEUTRAL PLANE   N. Pole

ARMATURE CORE

FIG. 55.

The axial length of the armature is supposed to be so great that the distribution of magnetic field may be taken as the same on all planes parallel to the paper. We then have a two-dimensional problem.

A further assumption is made that does not quite hold in practice, namely, that the surface of iron pole is at a uniform magnetic potential. In most dynamos the exciting coil comes down within an inch or two of the surface of the armature and the whole of the part below the pole is at approximately the same potential while the potentials of the parts more remote from the armature become smaller and smaller as we travel up the exciting coil until we arrive at the root of the pole where the potential is nearly zero. As the amount of fringing field extending on the armature is only slightly affected by these circumstances, we may make the above assumption without seriously vitiating the usefulness of the results obtained.

If the armature surface is taken as zero potential, the neutral plane is also at zero potential so we arrive at the simple geometrical shape in the z-plane given in Fig. 56, where XBC represents a surface at the magnetic potential of the pole and DOF represents a surface at zero magnetic potential. The lines at X and D may be taken to extend to infinity without changing the value of the fringing flux, and also the lines at C and F may extend to infinity. We will denote the length of the air-gap by g and the distance from the

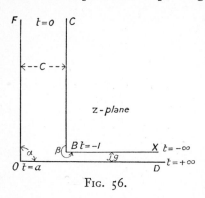

FIG. 56.

side of the pole to the neutral line by c. When we come to straighten out $XBCFOD$ on the horizontal axis of the t-plane (see Fig. 57), some judgement is required in deciding what point in the z-plane shall correspond with $t = 0$ in the t-plane. After a few trials we find that it is convenient to take C and F as corresponding to $t = 0$. We may then arbitrarily take B as corresponding to $t = -1$, and O the origin in the z-plane as $t = a$. The value of a is afterwards shown to be equal to g^2/c^2.

t-plane

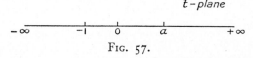

FIG. 57.

The angle at B ($= \beta$) is equal to three right angles so that the index $\left(\dfrac{\beta}{\pi} - 1\right) = \left(\dfrac{3\pi}{2} \times \dfrac{1}{\pi} - 1\right) = \tfrac{1}{2}$. As b has been taken equal to -1, $(t-b)^{(\beta/\pi)-1} = (t+1)^{\frac{1}{2}}$. The angle at C and F is zero, so that $(t-0)^{(0/\pi)-1} = t^{-1}$.

The angle at O is a right angle, so that

$$(t-a)^{\frac{\pi}{2} \times \frac{1}{\pi} - 1} = (t-a)^{-\frac{1}{2}}.$$

The equation for the transformation then is

$$\frac{dz}{dt} = A(t+1)^{\frac{1}{2}} t^{-1} (t-a)^{-\frac{1}{2}}.$$

We will first of all deal with the transition of t from one side of zero to the other by way of the minute semicircle of radius r, which we can make as small as we like. Over this range $t = re^{j\theta}$. This transition in the t-plane (see Fig. 58) corresponds to the

FIG. 58.

passage from C to F in the z-plane. By integrating the equation for the special case we can find the relation between a and c.

Differentiating $t = re^{j\theta}$,

$$dt = jre^{j\theta}\, d\theta.$$

$$dz = Aj(t+1)^{-\frac{1}{2}}(t-a)^{-\frac{1}{2}}\frac{re^{j\theta}}{t}\, d\theta.$$

In this special case t can be neglected in comparison with 1 and a and it also cancels out with $re^{j\theta}$.

$$\int_c^0 dz = jA(-a)^{-\frac{1}{2}}\int_\pi^0 d\theta.$$

While θ changes from π to 0, z changes from c to 0.

$$-c = \frac{-j\pi A}{j\sqrt{a}}. \quad \therefore \quad c = \frac{\pi A}{\sqrt{a}},$$

or

$$a = \frac{\pi^2 A^2}{c^2}.$$

Next we will deal with the transition of t from $+\infty$ to $-\infty$ by way of a semicircle of infinite radius which swings through the angle π.

For this range let $t = Re^{j\theta}$, where R is an infinite radius. Then

$$dt = jRe^{j\theta}\, d\theta.$$

Also $(t+1)$ and $(t-a)$ can both be taken as $Re^{j\theta}$, and as the index of one is $\frac{1}{2}$ and of the other $-\frac{1}{2}$ they cancel out.

For this range then

$$\int_0^{jg} dz = A\frac{jRe^{j\theta}}{Re^{j\theta}}\int_0^\pi d\theta,$$

$$jg = j\pi A. \quad \therefore \quad A = \frac{g}{\pi}.$$

But from above $a = \dfrac{\pi^2 A^2}{c^2}$, $\therefore$ $a = \dfrac{g^2}{c^2}$.

The original equation thus becomes

$$\frac{dz}{dt} = \frac{g(t+1)^{\frac{1}{2}}}{\pi t(t-a)^{\frac{1}{2}}}.$$

The next step is to put into the t-plane a magnetic field such that we have a line of uniform magnetic potential (of say ψ_1) all along from $t = -\infty$ to $t = 0$, and a line of zero potential from $t = 0$ to $t = +\infty$. This we can do by taking another plane, the w-plane (shown in Fig. 59), in which we have a parallel distribution of

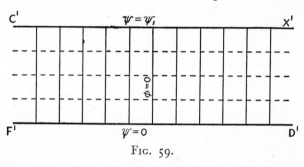

FIG. 59.

magnetic field so that $w = \phi + j\psi$. The line $F'D'$ is at zero potential and the line $C'X'$ is at potential ψ_1, the accented letters corresponding with the unaccented letters in the z-plane. Now imagine the line $X'C'$ folded back until it is in the same straight line with $F'D'$ so as to make the line $-\infty$ to $+\infty$ in the t-plane.

The Schwarzian transformation is simplest if we make the points C' and F' correspond with the point $t = 0$ in the t-plane. As the angle between $X'C'$ and $F'D'$ is zero, the index of $(t-0)$ in the transformation equation is $(0/\pi) - 1 = -1$, so that we have

$$\frac{dw}{dt} = B (t-0)^{-1} = B\frac{1}{t}.$$

As on p. 75, we begin by making the transition across the zero point by means of a minute semicircle. Over this range $t = r\epsilon^{j\theta}$ and $dt = jr\epsilon^{j\theta} d\theta$. Then

$$\int_0^{j\psi_1} dw = jB\frac{r\epsilon^{j\theta}}{r\epsilon^{j\theta}} \int_0^{\pi} d\theta,$$

$$j\psi_1 = j\pi B, \quad \therefore \quad B = \frac{\psi_1}{\pi}.$$

$$\frac{dw}{dt} = \frac{\psi_1}{\pi}\frac{1}{t},$$

$$w = \frac{\psi_1}{\pi}\log t + C = \frac{\psi_1}{\pi}(\log m + j\theta) + C.$$

Let $w = 0$ at the point o, where $t = a$.

$$w = \frac{\psi_1}{\pi}\log\frac{t}{a}, \text{ where } t = me^{j\theta}.$$

$$w = \frac{\psi_1}{\pi}(\log m + j\theta - \log a).$$

If the main object in view is to find the value of the magnetic flux-density on the surface of the armature, that is, along the axis of x in the z-plane, the procedure is much simpler than if we want a complete expression for ϕ and ψ throughout the fringing field.

Taking this case first, we observe that the flux-density $\mathbf{B} = \frac{d\phi}{dx}$, that is to say, that we are only concerned with the real values of w and the real values of z.

Now
$$\frac{dw}{dz} = \frac{dw}{dt} \times \frac{dt}{dz} = \frac{\psi_1}{\pi} \times \frac{1}{t} \times \frac{\pi t(t-a)^{\frac{1}{2}}}{g(t+1)^{\frac{1}{2}}}.$$

Write
$$\frac{\sqrt{t-a}}{\sqrt{t+1}} = u.$$

Then
$$\frac{dw}{dz} = \frac{\psi_1}{g}u,$$

or, on the real axis, the flux density

$$\mathbf{B} = \frac{d\phi}{dx} = \frac{\psi_1}{g}u = \frac{\psi_1}{g}\sqrt{\frac{t-a}{t+1}}.$$

To make use of this, we must find x in terms of u or in terms of t. This we do by integrating

$$\frac{dz}{dt} = \frac{g}{\pi t}\sqrt{\frac{t+1}{t-a}},$$

$$z = \frac{g}{\pi}\int \frac{1}{t}\sqrt{\frac{t+1}{t-a}}\, dt.$$

Let
$$u^2 = \frac{t-a}{t+1}.$$

Then $t = \dfrac{u^2+a}{1-u^2}$, $t+1 = \dfrac{1+a}{1-u^2}$, $(t+1)^2 = \dfrac{(1+a)^2}{(1-u^2)^2}$.

Differentiating u^2 we get

$$2u\, du = \frac{1+a}{(1+t)^2}\, dt; \quad dt = \frac{2u\, du\, (1+a)}{(1-u^2)^2},$$

$$z = \frac{g}{\pi} \int \frac{1-u^2}{u^2+a} \frac{1}{u} \frac{2u\, du\, (1+a)}{(1-u^2)^2} = \frac{2g}{\pi} \int \frac{(1+a)\, du}{(u^2+a)(1-u^2)},$$

$$z = \frac{2g}{\pi} \int \left(\frac{1}{u^2+a} + \frac{1}{1-u^2}\right) du$$

$$= \frac{2g}{\pi} \left\{\frac{1}{\sqrt{a}} \tan^{-1}\frac{u}{\sqrt{a}} + \tfrac{1}{2}\log\left(\frac{1+u}{1-u}\right)\right\} + K.$$

But
$$\sqrt{a} = \frac{g}{c},$$

$$z = \frac{2c}{\pi} \tan^{-1}\frac{cu}{g} + \frac{g}{\pi}\log\left(\frac{1+u}{1-u}\right) + K.$$

If we take the origin at the point o, $t = a$ and $u = 0$, hence $K = 0$.

As we have above the value of the flux-density **B** as a simple function of u,

$$\mathbf{B} = \frac{\psi_1}{g} u,$$

it is convenient to keep to the u in the expression for z rather than to convert to t.

On the real axis $z = x$, and we are only concerned with real values of t because the horizontal line a to $+\infty$ in the t-plane corresponds to OD in the z-plane. The value of **B** depends upon the ratio of c to g. In order to show how, plot the values of **B** for any ratio of c to g, let us take $g = 1$ and $c = 5$; $c/g = 5$. Take $\psi_1 = 1$.

$$x = 3\cdot1831 \tan^{-1}(5u) + 0\cdot31831 \log\left(\frac{1+u}{1-u}\right),$$

$$x = 3\cdot1831 \left(\tan^{-1}(5u) + \tfrac{1}{10}\log\frac{1+u}{1-u}\right) = 3\cdot1831 x_s.$$

Since $\psi_1 = 1$ and $g = 1$, $\mathbf{B} = u$.

TABLE OF VALUES FOR PLOTTING **B** OF FRINGING FIELD

u	$5u$	$\tan^{-1}5u$	$1+u$	$1-u$	$\dfrac{1+u}{1-u}$	$\log\dfrac{1+u}{1-u}$	x_s	x
0	0	0	1	1	1	0	0	0
0·1	0·5	0·4643	1·1	0·9	1·222	0·2005	0·4844	1·542
0·2	1·0	0·7854	1·2	0·8	1·5	0·4055	0·8260	2·629
0·3	1·5	0·9826	1·3	0·7	1·857	0·6190	1·0445	3·325
0·4	2·0	1·1074	1·4	0·6	2·333	0·8472	1·1921	3·795
0·5	2·5	1·1903	1·5	0·5	3·000	1·0986	1·3002	4·139
0·6	3·0	1·2497	1·6	0·4	4·000	1·3863	1·3883	4·419
0·7	3·5	1·2924	1·7	0·3	5·667	1·7347	1·4659	4·666
0·8	4·0	1·3259	1·8	0·2	9·000	2·1972	1·5456	4·920
0·9	4·5	1·3520	1·9	0·1	19·000	2·9444	1·6464	5·253
0·95	4·75	1·3631	1·95	0·05	39·000	3·6635	1·7295	5·505
0·97	4·85	1·3675	1·97	0·03	65·67	4·185	1·786	5·685
0·99	4·95	1·3716	1·99	0·01	199·0	5·293	1·901	6·051
1·00	5·0	1·3736	2·0	0·0	∞	∞	∞	∞

These values are plotted in Fig. 60.

This curve merely gives the value of the flux-density at various points on the surface of the armature. If we wish to make a complete plot of the lines of ϕ and ψ we revert to the expression (p. 77)

$$w = \phi + j\psi = \frac{\psi_1}{\pi}(\log m + j\theta - \log a),$$

$$\phi = \frac{\psi_1}{\pi}\log\frac{m}{a}.$$

For any particular line $\phi_0 = \dfrac{\psi_1}{\pi}\log\dfrac{m_0}{a}$,

$m_0 = a\epsilon^{\phi_0\pi/\psi_1}$, say $a\epsilon^p$,

$t = a\epsilon^{p+j\theta}$, say $a\epsilon^q$, where $q = p + j\theta$,

$$u = \sqrt{\frac{t-a}{t+1}} = \sqrt{\frac{a(\epsilon^q-1)}{\epsilon^q+1}},$$

$$z = x + jy = \frac{2c}{\pi}\tan^{-1}\left\{\sqrt{\frac{\epsilon^q-1}{\epsilon^q+1}}\right\} + \frac{g}{\pi}\log\left\{\frac{\sqrt{\epsilon^q+1}+\sqrt{a(\epsilon^q-1)}}{\sqrt{\epsilon^q+1}-\sqrt{a(\epsilon^q-1)}}\right\},$$

where

$$a = \frac{g^2}{c^2}.$$

By taking ϕ_0 constant, and taking various values of θ we obtain values for x and y in the z-plane.

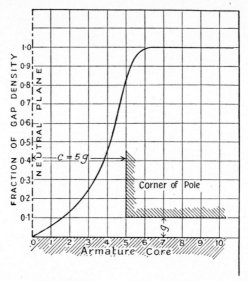

FIG. 60. Giving the flux-density on the surface of an armature due to the fringing from the corner of the pole. The values are given as fractions of the density in the gap far away from the corner.

Reverting to the expression

$$\phi + j\psi = \frac{\psi_1}{\pi}(\log m + j\theta - \log a),$$

$$\psi = \frac{\psi_1}{\pi}\theta.$$

To get any particular line $\psi = \psi_0$ we have $\psi_0 = \frac{\psi_1}{\pi}\theta_0$, giving

$$\theta_0 = \frac{\pi\psi_0}{\psi_1} = \text{say } Q,$$

$$t = m\epsilon^{jQ} \quad \text{and} \quad u = \sqrt{\frac{m\epsilon^{jQ} - a}{m\epsilon^{jQ} + 1}},$$

$$z = x + jy = \frac{2c}{\pi}\tan^{-1}\left\{\sqrt{\frac{m\epsilon^{jQ} - a}{a(m\epsilon^{jQ} + 1)}}\right\} + \frac{g}{\pi}\log\left\{\frac{\sqrt{m\epsilon^{jQ} + 1} + \sqrt{m\epsilon^{jQ} - a}}{\sqrt{m\epsilon^{jQ} + 1} - \sqrt{m\epsilon^{jQ} - a}}\right\}.$$

EXAMPLE NO. 9

DYNAMO SLOTS

THE EFFECT ON THE RELUCTANCE OF AN AIR-GAP OF THE PRESENCE OF DEEP ARMATURE SLOTS

IN Fig. 61 let the line E_1C_2 represent the projection of part of a pole face, and the lines C_1BA_2, A_1FE_2 the projections of the

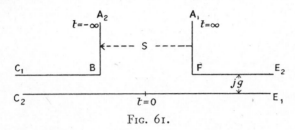

FIG. 61.

corners of a deep slot of width s. The width of the gap is g and as in Fig. 56 its direction is vertical: it is shown as jg.

Let us open out this figure into a straight line in the t-plane, taking A_1 to correspond with $t=\infty$, A_2 to correspond with $t=-\infty$, and the centre of symmetry shown in Fig. 61 corresponding to $t=0$ in Fig. 62.

The angles B and F are $\frac{3}{2}\pi$ and the angles at C and E are 0, so that

$$\frac{dz}{dt} = H(t-b)^{\frac{1}{2}}(t-c)^{-1}(t-e)^{-1}(t-f)^{\frac{1}{2}},$$

where the points b, c, e, and f correspond to the points B, C, E, and F respectively in the z-plane.

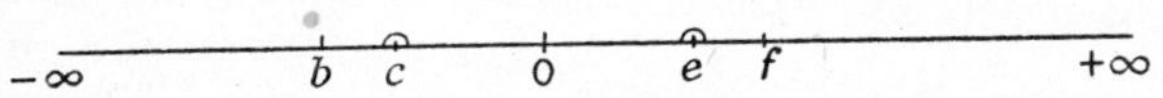

t – Plane

$-\infty$ b c 0 e f $+\infty$

FIG. 62.

From the symmetry of this figure we get $b=-f$ and $c=-e$.

$$b^2 = f^2 \quad \text{and} \quad c^2 = e^2.$$

$$\therefore \quad \frac{dz}{dt} = H\frac{(t^2-f^2)^{\frac{1}{2}}}{(t+e)(t-e)}.$$

To find H, integrate over an infinitely small semicircle of radius r at the point $t=e$.

M

Let $(t-e) = re^{j\theta}$, where r is an infinitely small radius and $dt = jre^{j\theta} \, d\theta$.

$$\int_0^{jg} dz = jH \int_\pi^0 \frac{(t^2-f^2)^{\frac{1}{2}}re^{j\theta}}{re^{j\theta}(t+e)} \, d\theta,$$

$$jg = -j\pi H \frac{(e^2-f^2)^{\frac{1}{2}}}{2e}. \qquad \therefore \quad H = -\frac{2ge}{\pi j(f^2-e^2)^{\frac{1}{2}}}.$$

Now integrate around a semicircle of infinitely large radius, so that $t = Re^{j\theta}$, where R is infinitely long. $dt = jRe^{j\theta} \, d\theta$; as f is negligible $(t^2-f^2)^{\frac{1}{2}} = Re^{j\theta}$.

$$\int_{A_1}^{A_2} dz = jH \int_0^\pi \frac{Re^{j\theta} \times Re^{j\theta} \, d\theta}{R^2 e^{j2\theta}},$$

$$-s = j\pi H. \qquad \therefore \quad H = -\frac{s}{\pi j} = -\frac{2ge}{\pi j(f^2-e^2)^{\frac{1}{2}}}.$$

$$\frac{g}{s} = \frac{(f^2-e^2)^{\frac{1}{2}}}{2e} = -\frac{(f^2-c^2)^{\frac{1}{2}}}{2c}.$$

$$\frac{dz}{dt} = -\frac{s\sqrt{t^2-f^2}}{\pi j(t^2-e^2)} = \frac{s\sqrt{f^2-t^2}}{\pi(t^2-e^2)} = \frac{s\sqrt{f^2-t^2}}{\pi(t^2-c^2)}.$$

For the w-plane let us take an air-gap with the slot reduced to a negligible width as in Fig. 63.

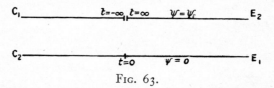

FIG. 63.

Put into this w-plane a uniform magnetic field such that the magnetic lines go vertically from $E_2 C_1$ to $E_1 C_2$. Let the flux function be denoted by ϕ and the magnetic potential by ψ, so that

$$w = \phi + j\psi.$$

Take the magnetic potential of the line $E_1 C_2$ at zero and that of $E_2 C_1 = \psi_1$.

Open out the figure as before taking $t = 0$ at the centre of symmetry and the points corresponding to $t = \infty$ and $t = -\infty$ as shown in Fig. 64.

As the angles at B and F are absent we have

$$\frac{dw}{dt} = G(t-c)^{-1}(t-e)^{-1}, \text{ where } c = -e,$$

$$= G\frac{1}{t^2-c^2} = G\frac{1}{t^2-e^2}.$$

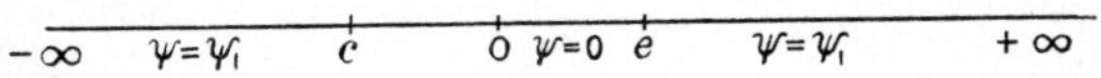

$$-\infty \quad \psi=\psi_1 \quad c \quad 0 \; \psi=0 \; e \quad \psi=\psi_1 \quad +\infty$$

Fig. 64.

Taking $t = e$ and integrating from $\psi = 0$ to $\psi = \psi_1$, we get

$$j\psi_1 = -j\pi G\frac{1}{2e}. \qquad \therefore \quad G = -\frac{2e\psi_1}{\pi}.$$

$$\frac{dw}{dt} = -\frac{2e\psi_1}{\pi}\frac{1}{(t^2-e^2)},$$

$$\frac{dw}{dz} = \frac{dw}{dt}\times\frac{dt}{dz} = -\frac{2e\psi_1}{\pi}\frac{1}{t^2-e^2}\times\frac{\pi(t^2-e^2)}{s\sqrt{f^2-t^2}}.$$

If we take $\dfrac{dw}{dz}$ along the axis of x only we get

$$\frac{d\phi}{dx} = -\frac{2e\psi_1}{s\sqrt{f^2-t^2}}.$$

The rate of change of the flux function along the axis of x is of course the vertical flux-density. So the last given expression gives us the value of the vertical flux-density for any real value of t.

If we were to integrate this between c and e we should get an

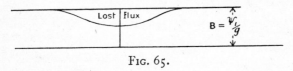

Fig. 65.

infinite amount of flux; so to keep to a finite integral we may subtract the flux-density for the case where there is a slot from the uniform flux-density where there is no slot. When there is no slot the flux-density all along has the same value as at $t = e$. That is to say,

$$\frac{d\phi_e}{dx} = -\frac{2e\psi_1}{s\sqrt{f^2-e^2}} = \frac{\psi_1}{g} \quad \text{(see Fig. 65)}.$$

Subtracting the flux-densities for the two different cases and substituting for dz its value $\dfrac{s\sqrt{f^2-t^2}}{\pi(t^2-e^2)}$ we get

$$d\phi_e - d\phi = \frac{2e\psi_1}{\pi\sqrt{f^2-e^2}}\left\{\frac{\sqrt{f^2-t^2}-\sqrt{f^2-e^2}}{e^2-t^2}\right\}dt.$$

The expression has been made positive by writing (e^2-t^2) instead of (t^2-e^2). The integral will give us the lost flux indicated in Fig. 69.

To integrate this expression it is well to make certain substitutions which can be followed easily by examining Figs. 66 and 67.

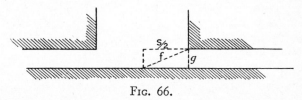

FIG. 66.

In Fig. 66 the slot and gap are drawn to scale showing a rectangle having the sides g and $s/2$ with a diagonal marked f. Now draw another figure in the t-plane in which e takes the place of $s/2$.

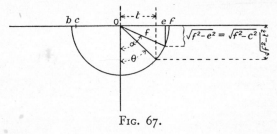

FIG. 67.

It was proved above that

$$\frac{2g}{s} = \frac{\sqrt{f^2-e^2}}{e} = -\frac{\sqrt{f^2-c^2}}{c} = \frac{\cos\alpha}{\sin\alpha} = \cot\alpha,$$

$$\sqrt{f^2-e^2} = f\cos\alpha; \qquad e = f\sin\alpha.$$

Consider further the variable angle θ in Fig. 67. Here the real part of the variable t has been taken less than e. The angle θ is such that $f\cos\theta = \sqrt{f^2-t^2}$,

$$f\sin\theta = t; \qquad dt = f\cos\theta\,d\theta.$$

Also $\qquad t^2 = f^2 \sin^2\theta \quad \text{and} \quad e^2 = f^2 \sin^2\alpha.$

Substituting in the expression on p. 84 we get

$$\int_{-\infty}^{+\infty} d\phi_e - \int_{-\infty}^{+\infty} d\phi = \frac{2e\psi_1}{\pi f \cos\alpha} \int_{-\alpha}^{+\alpha} \frac{\cos\theta - \cos\alpha}{\sin^2\alpha - \sin^2\theta} \cos\theta \, d\theta.$$

Write $\qquad \dfrac{2e\psi_1}{\pi f \cos\alpha} = A$

and $\sin^2\alpha - \sin^2\theta = \cos^2\theta - \cos^2\alpha = (\cos\theta + \cos\alpha)(\cos\theta - \cos\alpha).$

Also $$\int_{-\alpha}^{+\alpha} = 2\int_{0}^{+\alpha}.$$

$$\text{Integral} = 2A \int_{0}^{\alpha} \frac{1}{\cos\theta + \cos\alpha} \cos\theta \, d\theta.$$

$$\phi_e - \phi = 2A \int_{0}^{\alpha} \left(1 - \frac{\cos\alpha}{\cos\theta + \cos\alpha}\right) d\theta.$$

Consider the expression

$$\frac{\cos\alpha}{\cos\theta + \cos\alpha} = \cot\alpha \frac{\sin\alpha}{\cos\theta + \cos\alpha}$$

$$= \tfrac{1}{2}\cot\alpha \frac{\sin\left(\dfrac{\alpha-\theta}{2} + \dfrac{\alpha+\theta}{2}\right)}{\cos\dfrac{\alpha-\theta}{2}\cos\dfrac{\alpha+\theta}{2}}$$

$$= \tfrac{1}{2}\cot\alpha \frac{\sin\dfrac{\alpha-\theta}{2}\cos\dfrac{\alpha+\theta}{2} + \cos\dfrac{\alpha-\theta}{2}\sin\dfrac{\alpha+\theta}{2}}{\cos\dfrac{\alpha-\theta}{2}\cos\dfrac{\alpha+\theta}{2}}.$$

Now

$$\int \tfrac{1}{2}\cot\alpha \left\{ \frac{\sin\dfrac{\alpha-\theta}{2}}{\cos\dfrac{\alpha-\theta}{2}} + \frac{\sin\dfrac{\alpha+\theta}{2}}{\cos\dfrac{\alpha+\theta}{2}} \right\} d\theta$$

$$= \int \cot\alpha \left\{ \frac{d\log\cos\dfrac{\alpha-\theta}{2}}{d\theta} - \frac{d\log\cos\dfrac{\alpha+\theta}{2}}{d\theta} \right\} d\theta = \cot\alpha \log \frac{\cos\dfrac{\alpha-\theta}{2}}{\cos\dfrac{\alpha+\theta}{2}}.$$

When $\theta = \alpha$, this becomes $\cot\alpha\log\dfrac{1}{\cos\alpha} = \cot\alpha\log\sec\alpha$. If we integrate from $-\alpha$ to $+\alpha$ we get twice this amount. Now return to the original whole expression and fill in the value for A, carrying the $\cos\alpha$ in the denominator into the bracket. The total flux lost (see Fig. 69) through the presence of the slot is

$$\phi_e - \phi = \frac{2e\psi_1}{\pi f}\left(\frac{2\alpha}{\cos\alpha} - \frac{2}{\sin\alpha}\log\sec\alpha\right),$$

$$\frac{e}{f} = \sin\alpha,$$

$$\phi_e - \phi = \frac{4\psi_1}{\pi}\{\alpha\tan\alpha - \log\sec\alpha\},$$

$$\tan\alpha = \frac{s}{2g}.$$

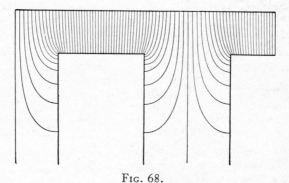

FIG. 68.

Dr. F. W. Carter in making the correction for the effect of a slot uses the symbol σ in the following manner. Consider a width σs less than s and assume that the flux instead of fringing as in Fig. 68 is arranged as in Fig. 69, there being no flux over σs, while over $s-\sigma s$ the flux-density is the same as in the uniform gap. Then the lost flux indicated in Fig. 65 (taken of course on a strip 1 cm. wide in the direction of the axial length of the armature) will be

$$\sigma s \times \frac{d\phi_e}{dx} = \phi_e - \phi;$$

but
$$\frac{d\phi_e}{dx} = \frac{2\psi_1}{s} \frac{e}{\sqrt{f^2-e^2}} = \frac{2\psi_1}{s}\tan\alpha.$$

$$\therefore \quad \sigma = \frac{\phi_e-\phi}{2\psi_1\tan\alpha},$$

$$\sigma = \frac{2}{\pi}\{\alpha - \cot\alpha\,\log\sec\alpha\},$$

$$s\sigma = \frac{2}{\pi}\left\{s\tan^{-1}\frac{s}{2g} - 2g\log\sqrt{1+\frac{s^2}{4g^2}}\right\}.$$

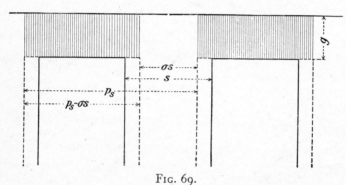

FIG. 69.

This is Carter's result. The values of σ for different values of s/g are plotted on p. 1117 of vol. lxiv of *Journ. Inst. Elec. Engineers* (1926).

If we wish to plot the lines of force as shown in Fig. 68 we must integrate the expression:

$$dz = H\frac{(t^2-f^2)^{\frac{1}{2}}}{(t+e)(t-e)}$$

This can be done by following the general method indicated in Example No. 8. As we have the connexion between w and t, where the w-plane contains a simple parallel magnetic field, $\phi+j\psi$, we can fill in the values of t after the manner indicated on p. 80.

EXAMPLE NO. 10

MAGNETIZED PLATE

TO transform the simple parallel magnetic field in the w-plane (Fig. 70) into that shown in the z-plane in Fig. 71. In this figure the lines ICB are to be at zero potential corresponding to ICB in Fig. 70. Both sides of the line JA and AB' are to be at potential ψ_1 corresponding to JAB' in Fig. 70. The line CB may represent the surface of an armature and AB' a pole face or JAB'

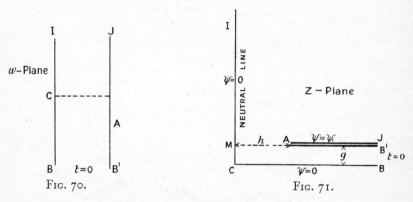

FIG. 70.   FIG. 71.

a plate of permeable material at potential ψ_1 placed in a permeable corner ICB at zero potential. The upper side of the line AJ may be regarded as the upper side of a pole tip when the latter is extremely attenuated. The result is employed in the next example to calculate the flux from a normal pole tip after the manner proposed by Dr. F. W. Carter.*

It will be noted that in Fig. 59 (p. 76) the real (horizontal) axis was taken as the equipotential line, $\psi = 0$, so that points along its length represent various values of ϕ. The vertical axis was taken as the axis along which to set off various values of ψ. We were able to write

$$w = \phi + j\psi.$$

But in Fig. 70 the potential function varies as we move horizontally and the flux function as we move vertically, so that for this figure we write

$$w = \psi + j\phi.$$

* 'The magnetic field of the dynamo-electric machine': *J.I.E.E.*, vol. lxiv, p. 1115.

As the student should get used to working the problem either way, we show below (p. 90) the difference in the result when $v = \phi + j\psi$. Let the width of the gap $= g$ and the distance of A from IC shown by the dotted line $MA = h$.

First transform Fig. 71 into the t-plane in Fig. 72.

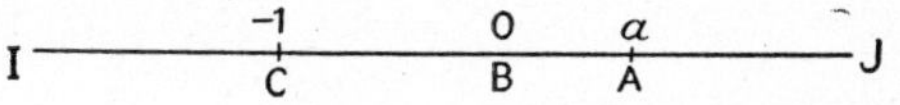

$$I \overline{\quad\underset{\underset{C}{-1}}{\quad}\quad\quad\underset{\underset{B}{0}}{\quad}\underset{\underset{A}{a}}{\quad}\quad\quad} J$$

Fig. 72.

$$\frac{dz}{dt} = \frac{M(t-a)}{(t+1)^{\frac{1}{2}}t},$$

where M is a positive constant. The angle at A is 2π, so that $\left(\dfrac{\alpha}{\pi} - 1\right) = \left(\dfrac{2\pi}{\pi} - 1\right) = 1$. At a point near to $t = 0$, let $t = re^{j\theta}$, $dt = jt\,d\theta$.

$$\int_0^{jg} dz = \frac{jM(-a)}{t}\, t \int_\pi^0 d\theta,$$

$$jg = j\pi Ma. \quad\therefore\quad M = \frac{g}{\pi a},$$

$$dz = \frac{g}{\pi a}\frac{(t-a)}{(t+1)^{\frac{1}{2}}t}\, dt. \tag{1}$$

Next transform the parallel field in the w-plane into the same t-plane:

$$\frac{dw}{dt} = j\frac{N}{t}.$$

The j turns the whole of Fig. 70 through one right angle.

Near $t = 0$, let $t = re^{j\theta}$, $\qquad dt = jt\,d\theta$,

$$\int_0^{\psi_1} dw = -N \int_\pi^0 d\theta,$$

$$\psi_1 = N\pi. \quad\therefore\quad N = \frac{\psi_1}{\pi}.$$

$$\therefore\quad dw = j\frac{\psi_1}{\pi}\frac{dt}{t},$$

$$w = \frac{j\psi_1}{\pi}\log t + \text{const.}$$

N

Now from Figs. 70, 71 and 72,

$$w = 0 \text{ when } t = -1 = \epsilon^{j\pi}, \qquad \log(-1) = j\pi.$$

$$0 = \frac{j\psi_1}{\pi} \times j\pi + \text{const.} \quad \therefore \quad \text{const.} = \psi_1.$$

$$\psi + j\phi = w = \psi_1\{1 + (j/\pi)\log t\}. \tag{2}$$

Along the line ICB where $\psi = 0$ we have

$$j\phi = \psi_1\{1 + (j/\pi)\log t\}.$$

$$\therefore \quad \log t = \frac{\pi\phi}{\psi_1} + j\pi.$$

$$\therefore \quad t = -\epsilon^{\pi\phi/\psi_1}. \tag{3}$$

The reason why the sign is different (minus instead of plus) when the result is compared with a similar expression on p. 58 is that in the present case the point $t = 0$ is made to correspond with BB' in Fig. 70, the higher magnetic potential ψ_1 being on the right; whereas in connexion with Figs. 44 and 45, the point corresponding to $t = 0$ was $M'N'$, the higher value of the stream function C being on the left. Our reason for giving the parallel magnetic field as it is done in Fig. 70 is that the student may appreciate the differences in the methods of attack. To make this point clear we will transform the magnetic field in Fig. 73 into the t-plane illustrated in Fig. 74.

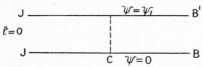

FIG. 73. The v-plane in which the lines representing $\psi = $ const. are horizontal.

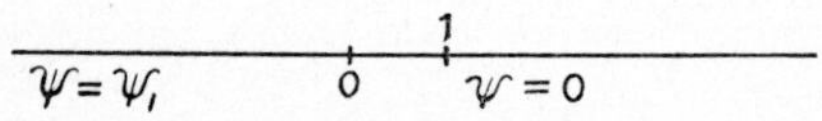

FIG. 74. The t-plane resulting from the opening out of Fig. 73.

$$v = \phi + j\psi,$$

$$\frac{dv}{dt} = \frac{\psi_1}{\pi}\frac{1}{t},$$

$$\int dv = \frac{\psi_1}{\pi}\int \frac{1}{t}\,dt,$$

$$v = \frac{\psi_1}{\pi}\log t + \text{const.}$$

When $t = 1$, let $v = 0$; then const. $= 0$.

$$v = \frac{\psi_1}{\pi} \log t,$$

$$\phi + j\psi = \frac{\psi_1}{\pi} \log t.$$

When t is positive and real, $\psi = 0$.

$$\therefore \quad \phi = \frac{\psi_1}{\pi} \log t,$$

$$\log t = \frac{\pi \phi}{\psi_1},$$

$$t = \epsilon^{\pi \phi / \psi_1},$$

the sign being opposite for the reason already given.

In comparing these two methods of introducing the rectangular distribution of ϕ and ψ we see that the more convenient is that represented by Fig. 73; for at a great distance to the right in Fig. 71 the distribution is such that the equipotential lines ($\psi = $ constant) are horizontal as they are in Fig. 73 and we therefore avoid the introduction of j in the expression for $\frac{dw}{dt}$.

We therefore write

$$w = \phi + j\psi$$

and

$$\frac{dw}{dt} = \frac{\psi_1}{\pi} \frac{1}{t}.$$

Returning now to the problem in the z-plane, the field strength at any point is

$$\frac{dw}{dz} = \frac{dw}{dt} \times \frac{dt}{dz} = \frac{\psi_1 \, a}{g} \times \frac{(t+1)^{\frac{1}{2}}}{(t-a)}.$$

When $t = 0$ this becomes ψ_1/g, that is, the difference in magnetic potential divided by the length of the gap. This is as it should be, for when t is small the corresponding point in the z-plane is far into the parallel part of the field.

Along the line CB in Fig. 71, where $\psi = 0$ and $z = x$,

$$\frac{dw}{dx} = \frac{\psi_1 \, a}{g} \times \frac{(t+1)^{\frac{1}{2}}}{t-a} \; * .$$

---

* This corresponds to Carter's formula (56) p. 1123, *J.I.E.E.*, vol. lxiv. See p. 96 below as to explanation of the other symbols. With Carter $\psi_1 = 1$.

To integrate (1) and find z, put $u = (t+1)^{\frac{1}{2}}$.

$$\frac{g}{\pi a}\left(1-\frac{a}{t}\right)\frac{dt}{(t+1)^{\frac{1}{2}}} = \frac{g}{\pi a}\left(1-\frac{a}{u^2-1}\right)2\,du.$$

Hence we may put either

$$dz = \frac{g}{\pi}\left(\frac{2}{a}-\frac{2}{u^2-1}\right)du, \tag{4}$$

or

$$dz = \frac{g}{\pi}\left(\frac{2}{a}+\frac{2}{1-u^2}\right)du. \tag{5}$$

From (4)

$$z = \frac{g}{\pi}\left(\frac{2u}{a}+\log\frac{u+1}{u-1}\right)+H; \tag{6}$$

from (5)

$$z = \frac{g}{\pi}\left(\frac{2u}{a}+\log\frac{1+u}{1-u}\right)+K. \tag{7}$$

(6) and (7) are the same; but (6) is appropriate for the pole face BAJ, where $t > 0$ ($u > 1$), and (7) for the armature face CB, where $-1 < t < 0$ ($0 < u < 1$).

On the pole face the imaginary part of z is the constant jg, and hence $H = jg$ in (6). On the armature face $z = 0$ when $t = -1$ ($u = 0$), hence $K = 0$ in (7). Hence

$$z = \frac{g}{\pi}\left[\frac{2}{a}(t+1)^{\frac{1}{2}}+\log\frac{(t+1)^{\frac{1}{2}}+1}{(t+1)^{\frac{1}{2}}-1}\right]+jg. \tag{8}$$

This form of the solution is suitable for the pole face [compare Carter's (45)]. Also

$$z = \frac{g}{\pi}\left[\frac{2}{a}(t+1)^{\frac{1}{2}}+\log\frac{1+(t+1)^{\frac{1}{2}}}{1-(t+1)^{\frac{1}{2}}}\right]. \tag{9}$$

This form is suitable for the armature face.

Now (9) can be written

$$z = \frac{g}{\pi}\left[\frac{2}{a}(t+1)^{\frac{1}{2}}+\log\frac{\{1+(t+1)^{\frac{1}{2}}\}^2}{-t}\right]. \tag{10}$$

Hence near B (where t is small and negative) on the armature face

$$x\,(=z) \doteqdot \frac{g}{\pi}\left[\frac{2}{a}+\log 4-\log(-t)\right]$$

or, by (10),

$$x \doteqdot \frac{g}{\pi}\left(\frac{2}{a}+\log 4-\frac{\pi\phi}{\psi_1}\right) \qquad \text{[Carter's (54)]}$$

and hence

$$-\phi \doteqdot \frac{\psi_1}{g}\left\{x-\frac{g}{\pi}\left(\frac{2}{a}+\log 4\right)\right\}.$$

That is to say, the flux reaching the armature on any length x measured from C is the same as though the field had its maximum strength ψ_1/g over the length

$$x - \frac{g}{\pi}\left(\frac{2}{a} + \log 4\right).$$

Or to put it another way, the total flux is the same as if the field had its maximum strength over the pole face increased in length at each tip by

$$h - \frac{g}{\pi}\left(\frac{2}{a} + \log 4\right).$$

The relation between a, g, and h is given by (8) when we put $t = a$. Since at A we have $z = h + jg$,

$$h = \frac{g}{\pi}\left[\frac{2}{a}(a+1)^{\frac{1}{2}} + \log \frac{(a+1)^{\frac{1}{2}}+1}{(a+1)^{\frac{1}{2}}-1}\right]. \tag{11}$$

Taking $g = 1$ (which is convenient for most purposes) a curve can be plotted giving the relation between h and a. Thus when $a = 1$, $h = 1\cdot46$, and when $a = 0\cdot44$, $h = 2\cdot5$. The values of a are necessary for the formulae given below.

When we wish to express z in terms of ϕ and ψ the procedure varies very little whether we begin with the distribution in the w-plane like that in Fig. 73, in which

$$w = \phi + j\psi,$$

or whether we begin with the distribution like that in Fig. 71, in which

$$w = \psi + j\phi.$$

Taking the first alternative,

$$w = \phi + j\psi = \frac{\psi_1}{\pi}\log t,$$

$$\log t = \frac{\pi}{\psi_1}\phi + j\frac{\pi}{\psi_1}\psi.$$

Writing $\dfrac{\pi}{\psi_1} = k$, $\qquad t = \epsilon^{k\phi + jk\psi}$

$$= \epsilon^{k\phi}\{\cos k\psi + j\sin k\psi\}.$$

This is dealt with as shown below.

Or, starting with the alternative

$$w = \psi + j\phi = \psi_1 + j\frac{\psi_1}{\pi}\log t,$$

$$\log t = \frac{\pi}{\psi_1}\phi - j\frac{\pi}{\psi_1}(\psi - \psi_1).$$

Writing $k = \dfrac{\pi}{\psi_1}$, $\quad t = \epsilon^{k\phi - jk(\psi - \psi_1)}.$

We can now substitute this value of t in equation (8).

In finding the real and imaginary parts of z for any given values of ϕ and ψ, it is well to make use of the form

$$\epsilon^{k\phi - jk(\psi - \psi_1)} = \epsilon^{k\phi}\{\cos k(\psi - \psi_1) - j\sin k(\psi - \psi_1)\}$$
$$= \epsilon^{k\phi}\{\cos k(\psi_1 - \psi) + j\sin k(\psi_1 - \psi)\}.$$

For brevity write $\beta = k(\psi_1 - \psi)$. Then

$$t = \epsilon^{k\phi}(\cos\beta + j\sin\beta).$$

The value of $(t+1)^{\frac{1}{2}}$ can then be obtained graphically as follows:

$$\beta = k\,(\psi_1 - \psi).$$

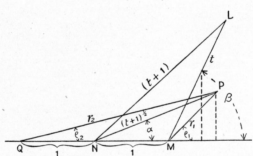

Fig. 75. Graphic construction for finding the value of $(t+1)^{\frac{1}{2}}$. The figure is reproduced twice full size for clearness.

Set off the angle β radians with a radius of 1 cm. as in Fig. 75. The horizontal and vertical components give $\cos\beta$ and $\sin\beta$ respectively. From tables obtain $\epsilon^{k\phi}$ and lay this off to scale at the angle β along ML. Set off MN 1 cm. to the left. Then $NL = (t+1)$. Take the square root of this length and set it off as shown, NP bisecting the angle at N. Let the length of $NP = m$,

$$(t+1)^{\frac{1}{2}} = m\epsilon^{j\alpha} = m\cos\alpha + jm\sin\alpha.$$

We can now change the sign of the log term in equation (8) by interchanging numerator and denominator, and write

$$z = \frac{g}{\pi}\left[\frac{2}{a}(m\cos\alpha + jm\sin\alpha) - \log\frac{(t+1)^{\frac{1}{2}}-1}{(t+1)^{\frac{1}{2}}+1}\right] + jg.$$

From Fig. 75 we see that the vector MP is $(t+1)^{\frac{1}{2}}-1$ and the vector QP is $(t+1)^{\frac{1}{2}}+1$. Writing the vectors in the form $r_1\epsilon^{j\rho_1}$ and $r_2\epsilon^{j\rho_2}$ respectively, and $\rho_1-\rho_2 = \rho$, we get

$$z = \frac{g}{\pi}\left[\frac{2m}{a}\cos\alpha - \log\frac{r_1}{r_2} + j\left(\frac{2m}{a}\sin\alpha - \rho\right)\right] + jg.$$

The real part gives x and the imaginary part jy.

If we keep ϕ constant and only change ψ, which is always less than ψ_1, the radius NL moves in a circle and the point P moves on a circle, so that we can quickly get a number of values for z for that ϕ. Then take another ϕ with another radius NP and get another lot of values of z.

Similar graphical methods will be found of service for evaluating expressions obtained from Schwarzian transformations.

EXAMPLE NO. 11

A POLE-PIECE WITH A ROUNDED TIP

THE problem is to find an equipotential line which, from the results of Example No. 10, is approximately the same shape as the pole tip of a dynamo, and hence the evaluation of the flux from the pole face and tip.

In Fig. 76 the dotted line marked $\psi = \mu$ is supposed to represent such an equipotential line. It is one of the lines between AJ and ICB. The distance h' from IC is the distance of the nose of the actual pole from the neutral line (or if there is a commutating pole then the distance from the iron of this pole). The curvature of the nose is supposed to be given and we have to fit in a line AJ like that in Fig. 76 or in Fig. 71 such that when it is at potential ψ_1 it will give the equipotential line $\psi = \mu$, having the required curvature and position of nose, and having the gap γ equal to the gap in the machine in question. At the point A' on the nose of the pole $x = h'$ and the radius of curvature $= \rho$.

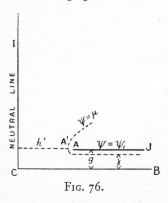

Fig. 76.

Put $\mu = (1-\lambda)\psi_1$. $\quad \therefore \quad \psi_1 = \dfrac{\mu}{1-\lambda}$. $\hfill (12)$

At a point well under the pole where the flux-density is constant

$$\frac{g}{\gamma} = \frac{\psi_1}{\mu} = \frac{1}{1-\lambda}. \qquad \therefore \quad g = \frac{\gamma}{1-\lambda}. \hfill (13)$$

In practice λ will be a fairly small fraction such as 0·2. So that g/γ may be about 1·25.

Along the equipotential $\psi = \mu$, we have from the last example (p. 94)

$$\mu + j\phi = \psi_1\{1 + (j/\pi)\log t\},$$

$$\psi_1(1-\lambda) + j\phi = \psi_1 + (j\psi_1/\pi)\log t,$$

$$\log t = \frac{\pi\phi}{\psi_1} + j\lambda\pi,$$

$$t = \epsilon^{\pi\phi/\psi_1} \times \epsilon^{j\lambda\pi}.$$

Write $t = q\epsilon^{j\lambda\pi}$, where q is the length of the vector t which varies from o to ∞ as ϕ varies from $-\infty$ to $+\infty$.

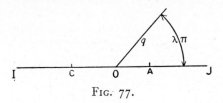

FIG. 77.

From (1), Example 10 (p. 89),

$$\frac{dz}{dt} = \frac{g}{\pi a} \frac{t-a}{(t+1)^{\frac{1}{2}}}.$$

Along $\psi = \mu$ put $dz = ds\epsilon^{j\theta}$, $t = q\epsilon^{j\lambda\pi}$. Then

$$\frac{ds}{dq}\epsilon^{j\theta} = \frac{g}{\pi a q} \frac{q\epsilon^{j\lambda\pi}-a}{(q\epsilon^{j\lambda\pi}+1)^{\frac{1}{2}}}.$$

In Fig. 78, let ML represent $q\epsilon^{j\lambda\pi}$. Then AL is

$$(q\epsilon^{j\lambda\pi}-a) = r_3\epsilon^{j\delta},$$

where

$$r_3 = (q^2+a^2-2aq\cos\lambda\pi)^{\frac{1}{2}}$$

and

$$\delta = \tan^{-1}\frac{q\sin\lambda\pi}{q\cos\lambda\pi-a}.$$

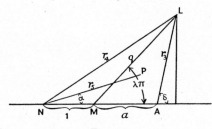

FIG. 78.

Further,

$$(q\epsilon^{j\lambda\pi}+1)^{\frac{1}{2}} = NP = r_5\epsilon^{j\alpha},$$

where

$$r_4 = (q^2+1+2q\cos\lambda\pi)^{\frac{1}{2}},$$

$$r_5 = r_4^{\frac{1}{2}} = (q^2+1+2q\cos\lambda\pi)^{\frac{1}{4}},$$

and

$$\alpha = \tfrac{1}{2}\tan^{-1}\frac{q\sin\lambda\pi}{q\cos\lambda\pi+1}.$$

o

Therefore
$$\frac{ds}{dq} = \frac{g}{\pi a q}\frac{(q^2+a^2-2aq\cos\lambda\pi)^{\frac{1}{2}}}{(q^2+1+2q\cos\lambda\pi)^{\frac{1}{2}}} \tag{14}$$

$$= \frac{g}{\pi a q}\frac{r_3}{r_5},$$

and
$$\theta = \tan^{-1}\frac{q\sin\lambda\pi}{q\cos\lambda\pi-a} - \tfrac{1}{2}\tan^{-1}\frac{q\sin\lambda\pi}{q\cos\lambda\pi+1}. \tag{15}$$

Differentiating with regard to q (λ being constant),

$$\frac{d\theta}{dq} = -\sin\lambda\pi\left[\frac{a}{q^2+a^2-2aq\cos\lambda\pi}+\frac{1}{2(q^2+1+2q\cos\lambda\pi)}\right] \tag{16}$$

$$= -\sin\lambda\pi\left(\frac{a}{r_3^2}+\frac{1}{2r_5^4}\right).$$

The radius of curvature of the equipotential line is given by

$$\frac{ds}{d\theta} = -\frac{g}{\pi a q\sin\lambda\pi}\left(\frac{2r_3^3 r_5^3}{2ar_5^4+r_3^2}\right).$$

At A', $\theta = \tfrac{1}{2}\pi$ and from (15)

$$\pi+\tan^{-1}\frac{q\sin\lambda\pi}{q\cos\lambda\pi+1} = 2\tan^{-1}\frac{q\sin\lambda\pi}{q\cos\lambda\pi-a}.$$

$$\therefore \quad \frac{q\sin\lambda\pi}{q\cos\lambda\pi+1} = \frac{2q\sin\lambda\pi(q\cos\lambda\pi-a)}{(q\cos\lambda\pi-a)^2-q^2\sin^2\lambda\pi}.$$

Whence
$$q^2+2q\cos\lambda\pi+1 = (a+1)^2. \tag{17}$$

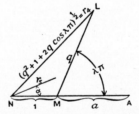

Fig. 79. Graphic construction showing the length of r_4 equal to $(a+1)$ in the special case where z is at A' in Fig. 69. In this special case the angle α from Fig. 78 is called β in the text.

So the diagram in the t-plane becomes like Fig. 79, where ML is the vector q corresponding to the vector to A' in the z-plane and the radius NL is equal to $NA = 1+a$. We thus have the value of q at A' in terms of a and λ (see later, p. 100, as to the taking of experimental values of a and λ). We can now simplify (14) and (16) for the point A' where we want to use them.

$$2aq\cos\lambda\pi = a(a^2+2a-q^2),$$

and hence
$$q^2+a^2-2aq\cos\lambda\pi = (q^2-a^2)(1+a), \tag{18}$$

and (14) becomes at A'

$$\frac{ds}{dq} = \frac{g}{\pi aq}(q^2-a^2)^{\frac{1}{2}}. \tag{19}$$

Using (17) and (18), (16) reduces to

$$\frac{d\theta}{dq} = -\sin\lambda\pi\left[\frac{q^2+a^2+2a}{2(q^2-a^2)(1+a)^2}\right]. \tag{20}$$

From (19) and (20) we now have the radius of curvature at A'

$$\rho = \frac{ds}{d\theta} = -\frac{2g}{\pi aq\sin\lambda\pi}\frac{(q^2-a^2)^{\frac{3}{2}}(1+a)^2}{(q^2+a^2+2a)}. \tag{21}$$

The radius of curvature can be rapidly evaluated for various experimental values of λ and a by setting off a diagram like Fig. 79 to scale.

To find h' in terms of a, g, and λ we have, at A',

$$(t+1)^{\frac{1}{2}} = (q\epsilon^{j\lambda\pi}+1)^{\frac{1}{2}}, \quad \text{where} \quad q^2+2q\cos\lambda\pi+1 = (a+1)^2,$$
$$= p\epsilon^{j\beta}, \quad \text{where} \quad p = (q^2+2q\cos\lambda\pi+1)^{\frac{1}{2}} = (a+1)^{\frac{1}{2}},$$
$$\text{and} \quad \beta = \tfrac{1}{2}\tan^{-1}\frac{q\sin\lambda\pi}{q\cos\lambda\pi+1}.$$

Hence, from (7), at A'

$$z = \frac{g}{\pi}\left\{\frac{2}{a}p\epsilon^{j\beta}+\log\frac{p\epsilon^{j\beta}+1}{p\epsilon^{j\beta}-1}\right\}+jg,$$

and since h' is the real part of z at A,

$$h' = \frac{g}{\pi}\left\{\frac{2}{a}p\cos\beta+\log\frac{p^2+1+2p\cos\beta}{p^2+1-2p\cos\beta}\right\}. \tag{22}$$

Since $g = \dfrac{\gamma}{(1-\lambda)}$, the values of e/γ and h'/γ are determined by (21) and (22) in terms of a and λ.

The pole face must now be increased by $h'-\dfrac{g}{\pi}\left(\dfrac{2}{a}+\log 4\right)$ to obtain the fringing coefficient.

In the application to an actual machine we know γ, h', and the radius of curvature.

Give various values to a in (11), p. 93, to discover what values of a give values of h/g that may be expected to lead to practical values of h'/γ. For example, putting $a = 1$ we find $h/g \doteqdot 1\frac{1}{2}$. Smaller values of a will give bigger values of h/g. In practice the values of h/g vary between 2 and 20.

For every reasonable value of a and a set of suitable values of λ:

Calculate q from (17).

  „ ρ/γ from (21), putting $g = \dfrac{\gamma}{1-\lambda}$.

  „ h'/γ from (22), putting $g = \dfrac{\gamma}{1-\lambda}$.

Plot ρ/γ and h'/γ against λ for each value of a.

In a given practical case pick out from the graphs the values of a and λ that appear to give the best approximation to ρ/γ and h'/γ presented in the case under consideration.

Carter has given in his Fig. 17, p. 1123 of vol. lxiv *J.I.E.E.*, values of the fringing coefficient for various ratios of ρ/γ and various values of h/γ. The fringe is equal to a conventional belt of flux of width

$$\left\{h - \frac{g}{\pi}\left(\frac{2}{a} + \log 4\right)\right\} = b \text{ (see Fig. 80)}$$

with flux density ψ_1/g. The fringing coefficient is the ratio of b to γ.

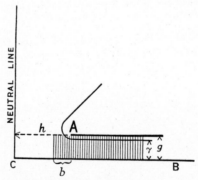

FIG. 80. Showing a belt of flux of width b and flux-density ψ_1/g. The flux in this belt is equal to the fringing flux from the pole tip.

Carter points out that where the armature face is slotted we should take for γ the equivalent gap G as determined by sections (3) and (4) of his paper.

EXAMPLE NO. 12

WHERE THE BOUNDARY IS PARTLY CIRCULAR

THE FLOW OF ELECTRIC CURRENT IN A LARGE CONDUCTING SHEET
IN WHICH THERE IS A CIRCULAR HOLE; OR THE FLOW OF ELECTRIC
CURRENT IN A LARGE BATH OF ELECTROLYTE AROUND A NON-
CONDUCTING CIRCULAR PILLAR.

THE problem is the same as that of the flow of a perfect
fluid past a round cylindrical obstruction at right angles
to its path.

Consider a conducting sheet having such a thickness and resistivity that there is a resistance of 1 ohm between opposite sides
of a square centimetre. If this sheet is infinite in extent, a parallel
flow of current in it gives rise to parallel equipotential lines and
the distribution can be expressed

$$t = V + jC \qquad \text{(p. 10)}.$$

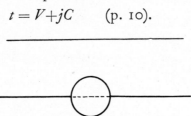

FIG. 81. A conducting sheet having a circular hole around which
current must pass.

Now let there be a circular hole in the sheet (see Fig. 81). Cut
the sheet in two along a diameter of the hole parallel to the flow
of current. By reason of the symmetry of the figure this will not
disturb the lines of flow. It gives us a half-infinite sheet which
we will denote as the z-plane.

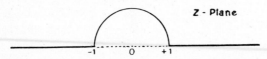

FIG. 82. Showing the boundary of z-plane which gives one line of flow
indicated by the full line.

It is required to find the transformation that converts the

boundary of this plane into a straight horizontal line in the *t*-plane.

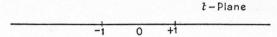

FIG. 83. It is required to convert the line of flow in Fig. 82 to the straight line in the *t*-plane as indicated in this figure.

Take the origin in the *z*-plane at the centre of the circle, and adjust the scales so that $+1$ lies on the circumference to the right of the centre, and -1 on the circumference to the left. We now show that $t = \frac{1}{2}(z+1/z)$ gives us the required transformation.

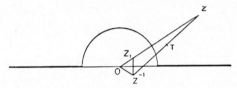

FIG. 84. Geometrical construction illustrating $t = \frac{1}{2}(z+1/z)$.

Take any vector $z = m\epsilon^{j\theta}$. Then $\dfrac{1}{z} = \dfrac{1}{m}\epsilon^{-j\theta}$. This, according to the rules of plotting complex quantities, is represented by a vector having a length $1/m$, and is set off with the negative θ below the axis of *x*. Denote the end of this vector by z^{-1}. Join zz^{-1} and bisect it at T. Then $OT = \frac{1}{2}(z+1/z) = t$.

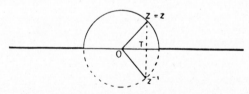

FIG. 85. Geometrical construction showing that if $t = \frac{1}{2}(z+1/z)$, a point in the *z*-boundary line of flow will fall on a straight horizontal line in the *t*-plane.

When *z* is greater than unity $1/m$ is smaller than unity, and if we set off the length $1/m = Oz_1$ along the direction of *z*, the point z_1 will fall within the circle. As *m* approaches unity $1/m$ also approaches unity, so that when *z* lies on the circle it coincides with z_1. Also z^{-1} falls on the dotted circle in Fig. 85 and *T* the point of bisection falls on the axis of *x*.

We see therefore that if *t* is a vector in the *t*-plane corresponding to z, such that $t = \frac{1}{2}(z+1/z)$, any point on the circle of radius 1 in the z-plane corresponds to a point on the horizontal axis in the t-plane. Further, we have seen (p. 1) that where the stream and potential functions satisfy Laplace's equation, it is only necessary to fit the stream-lines or equipotential lines to the appropriate boundary to solve the problem completely.

Solving for z we get*

$$z = t + \sqrt{t^2 - 1}.$$

It should be noted that the expression

$$t = \frac{1}{2}(z + 1/z),$$

in addition to transforming the t-plane into the z-plane, changes the scale in the z-plane to double. We can see that this is so because when z is very great, $1/z$ can be neglected in comparison and the expression approximates to $2t = z$.

If for instance $t = V + jC$, then at a great distance from the origin the expression gives us $z = 2V + j\,2C$.

We know that the small hole in the sheet makes hardly any change in the distribution at a great distance from it. It is therefore necessary to multiply the values of the corresponding stream-lines and equipotential lines by 2 in order to get their real values in a practical case. This is illustrated in the example given below.

The expression $t = V + jC$ gives the parallel distribution of stream-lines and equipotentials in the t-plane, where the horizontal line (Fig. 86) is the stream-line taken as zero, and the vertical line through $t = 0$ is taken as $V = 0$.

Cut a semicircular piece out of the sheet as shown in Fig. 87. Calculate the values of z from the expression

$$z = V + jC + \sqrt{(V+jC)^2 - 1}.$$

Keep C constant (say $= 1$) and vary V. For instance when $C = 1$ and $V = 0$,

$$z = 0 + j + \sqrt{(0+j)^2 - 1}$$
$$= j + j\sqrt{2} = j\,2\cdot414.$$

This is a vertical line $2\cdot414$ units long drawn through the origin. The value of the expression under the root sign can be found by

---

* The alternative $z = t - \sqrt{t^2 - 1}$ lies in the lower half-infinite sheet, that is, outside the problem.

putting it in the form $m\epsilon^{j\theta}$. Then $\sqrt{m\epsilon^{j\theta}} = \sqrt{m}\epsilon^{j\theta/2}$. It can be found graphically by plotting the expression under the root sign

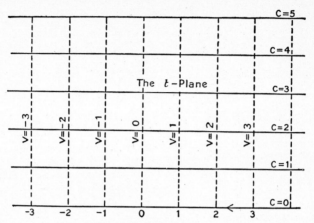

Fig. 86. Simple rectangular distribution of stream-lines and equipotential lines in the *t*-plane.

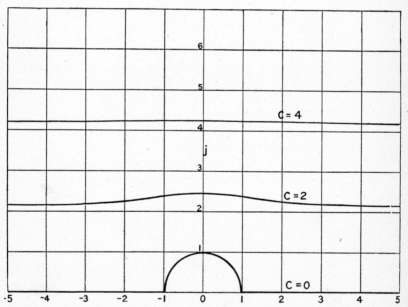

Fig. 87. Showing the disturbance to the lines of flow caused by a round hole in the *z*-plane.

and taking the square root of the distance m from the origin and setting this off at half the angle made by the vector $m\epsilon^{j\theta}$. If, for instance, t^2-1 makes an angle of $180°$ with the base line, then $\sqrt{t^2-1}$ is at right angles and of a length $\sqrt{m}$. If t^2-1 is at right angles, then $\sqrt{t^2-1}$ is at $45°$ to the base line. To this root we must always add $V+jC$. Taking a number of values for V with $C=1$ we get the middle stream-line plotted in Fig. 87. This, however, must not be labelled $C=1$ but $C=2$ for the reasons given above. Similarly we can get the equipotential lines by keeping V constant and working out values of z for various values of C. Here we must again multiply the values by 2 to get the corresponding equipotential line in the t-plane.

Differentiating the expression

$$z = t+\sqrt{t^2-1},$$

with regard to t, we get

$$\frac{dz}{dt} = \frac{t+\sqrt{t^2-1}}{\sqrt{t^2-1}}.$$

We are led to the conclusion that, in any transformation, if

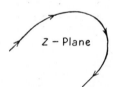

FIG. 88. Showing how the point in the z-plane moves round a curve turning to the right, the total change of direction being through $180°$.

$t+\sqrt{t^2-1}$ appears in the numerator of dz/dt, and if no other singular points occur between -1 and $+1$, then, while t moves along the real axis from -1 to $+1$, the corresponding point in the z-plane moves around on some curve, and its direction of motion turns through $180°$ to the right as indicated by Fig. 88.

If we replace $t+\sqrt{t^2-1}$ by $[t+\sqrt{t^2-1}]^n$ the direction of motion of z would ultimately have turned through $n\pi$ to the right. In particular, if $n=\frac{1}{2}$, we see that the insertion of $[t+\sqrt{t^2-1}]^{\frac{1}{2}}$ in the numerator, or $[\sqrt{t+1}+\sqrt{t-1}]$ in the numerator would turn the direction through $90°$ to the right.

It is interesting to observe the variation in z when t varies from

-1 to a value just a little greater, say $0.001-1$. When $t = -1$, $z = -1$. When $t = 0.001-1$,

$$t+\sqrt{t^2-1} = 0.001-1+j\,0.045,$$
$$\delta z = 0.001+j\,0.045.$$

The unreal or vertical component of the little change in z is 45 times as large as the real or horizontal component. That is to say, δz is nearly vertical. For the very smallest increase in t beyond -1 the track of z is vertical. Now consider $t = 0$,

$$t+\sqrt{t^2-1} = 0+\sqrt{0-1} = j.$$

A small increase in t, say 0.001, gives the same value to δz. That is to say, the track of z at this point is horizontal. For the value of $t = 1-0.001$ the track of z is almost vertically downwards.

Now consider the expression

$$z = t+\lambda\sqrt{t^2-1},$$

where λ is any constant. The introduction of the constant, though it alters the track of z, does not affect the properties of starting vertically upwards at $t = -1$, being horizontal at $t = 0$, and coming vertically downwards at $t = 1$. The λ merely multiplies

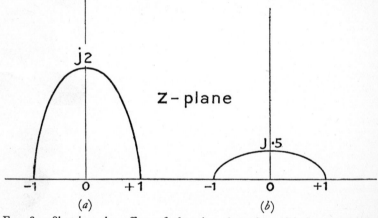

Fig. 89. Showing the effect of changing the value of λ in the expression $t+\lambda\sqrt{(t^2-1)}$. For the curve on the left $\lambda = 2$; for the curve on the right $\lambda = 0.5$.

the vertical component of z, as t moves horizontally from -1 to $+1$. For instance, if $\lambda = 2$ the track of z follows a curve like curve (a) in Fig. 89, and if $\lambda = 0.5$ the track is like curve (b).

The factor λ may also be introduced into the numerator mentioned on p. 105, which has the property of turning the track of z through 90°. Thus the terms $\sqrt{(t+1)}+\lambda\sqrt{(t-1)}$ in the numerator of the expression for the value of dz/dt has the effect of turning the track of z through 90° as r varies between -1 and $+1$. This expression is made use of in the next example.

EXAMPLE NO. 13

ROUNDED CORNERS

THE electrical stress in the vicinity of the rounded corners of a conductor forming part of a condenser has been investigated by* Dr. J. D. Cockcroft. His paper on the subject is a very good example of the application of the Schwarz-Christoffel transformation. It is not necessary to reproduce the paper here because it can easily be referred to by the student, but the following notes, due to Mr. F. Bowman, will be of assistance in getting over what is otherwise a rather difficult piece of work.

The case considered is that of two coaxial rectangular conductors, the edges of the inner conductor being rounded as shown in Fig. 90. These might form the conductors of an air condenser or represent the conductors inside an armature slot.

A potential difference is maintained between the conductors, each of which forms an equipotential surface. The problem is to determine the electrostatic stress in the vicinity of the corners. It is higher at the surface of the rounded corner than at any other part of the apparatus.

In the case under consideration the distances g and h are supposed to be small compared with the sides AG and EF, so that in Fig. 91 we need only consider one corner, the sides being supposed to extend to infinity.

The first step is to transform the horizontal line in the t-plane shown in Fig. 92 into the shape of Fig. 91.

$$\frac{dz}{dt} = -jM(t-a)^{-1}(t-b)^{-\frac{1}{2}}\{\sqrt{(t+1)}+\lambda\sqrt{(t-1)}\}.$$

The internal angle at A, where the corresponding value of $t = a$, is zero, so that $(\alpha/\pi-1) = -1$.

The internal angle at B, where the corresponding value of $t = b$, is $\frac{1}{2}\pi$, so that $(\beta/\pi-1) = -\frac{1}{2}$.

Between F and G the corresponding values of t are taken as passing from -1 to $+1$, and meanwhile the track of z turns

---

* 'The effect of curved boundaries on the distribution of electrical stress round conductors': *Journ. Inst. Electrical Engineers*, lxvi. 385.

through 90° to the right. This introduces the factor

$$\{\sqrt{(t+1)}+\lambda(t-1)\}.$$

With Fig. 91 in the position shown, the commencing line *EF* being

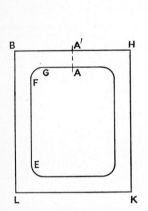

FIG. 90. Two concentric conductors, the internal one of which has rounded corners.

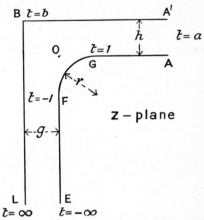

FIG. 91. One of the rounded corners of Fig. 90 in the case where *EF* is great as compared with *g*.

vertical while the *t* line is horizontal, the arbitrary constant should be unreal (see p. 89). Hence the $-jM$. Further, M may be taken as unity since we are not concerned with the absolute scale of the gap *g* upon which it depends (see p. 112).

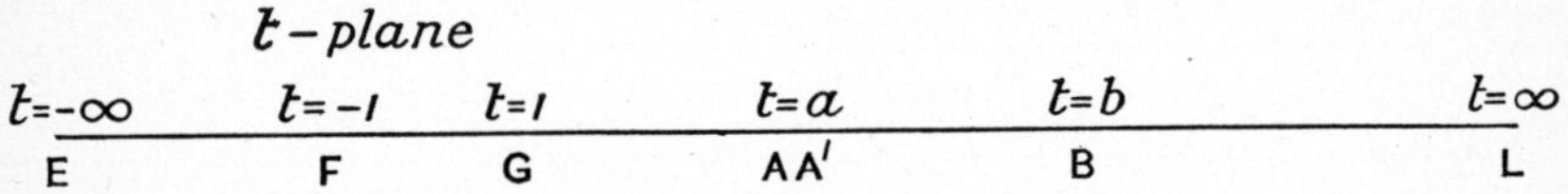

t–plane

$t=-\infty$	$t=-1$	$t=1$	$t=a$	$t=b$	$t=\infty$
E	F	G	A A'	B	L

FIG. 92. The horizontal line in the *t*-plane to which Fig. 91 has been opened out.

Integrating the above differential equation

$$z = -j \int \frac{\sqrt{(t+1)}+\lambda\sqrt{(t-1)}}{(t-a)\sqrt{(t-b)}}\, dt. \tag{1}$$

The next step is to put into the *t*-plane an electric field such that from $t = -\infty$ to $t = a$ the horizontal line is at one potential, say zero, and the horizontal line from $t = a$ to $t = +\infty$ at another potential, say ψ_1. This is done as on p. 90 by taking a rectangular field in the *w*-plane so that $w = \phi+j\psi$ (see Fig. 73).

ϕ is here the flux function and ψ the potential function. We then open out two parallel equipotential lines until they form the two lines FA and $A'L$ in the t-plane. As on p. 37,

$$\frac{dw}{dt} = K(t-a)^{-1}, \tag{2}$$

$$w = K \int \frac{dt}{t-a} = K \log(t-a) + C.$$

As shown on p. 5 we can eliminate the arbitrary constant of integration by taking real part of $w = 0$ at the point $t = a+1$. Further, we know from p. 37 that $K = \psi_1/\pi$. We are not, however, concerned with actual values of the potential function. By taking $\psi_1 = \pi$ we can take K at unity.

By combining (1) and (2) we get the electric stress

$$\frac{dw}{dz} = j \left| \frac{\sqrt{(t-b)}}{\sqrt{(t+1)} + \lambda \sqrt{(t-1)}} \right|. \tag{3}$$

Dr. Cockcroft has pointed out that by taking $\lambda = \sqrt{\dfrac{(b+1)}{(b-1)}}$ the value of electric stress over the curved corner (between $t = -1$ and $t = +1$) is constant and equal to $\sqrt{\dfrac{b-1}{2}}$. He therefore adopts this value for λ. Other multiplying factors would give different curves having a non-uniform stress over their length.

Fixing our attention upon values of t between -1 and $+1$, we put

$$j\sqrt{(1-t)} \quad \text{instead of} \quad \sqrt{(t-1)}$$
$$-(a-t) \quad \text{instead of} \quad (t-a)$$

and

$$j\sqrt{(b-t)} \quad \text{instead of} \quad \sqrt{(t-b)}.$$

Thus we get

$$z = \int \frac{\sqrt{(t+1)} + j\lambda\sqrt{(1-t)}}{(a-t)\sqrt{(b-t)}} \, dt \tag{4}$$

$$= \int \sqrt{\left(\frac{t+1}{b-t}\right)}\frac{dt}{(a-t)} + j\lambda \int \sqrt{\left(\frac{1-t}{b-t}\right)}\frac{dt}{(a-t)}$$

$$= I_1 + j\lambda I_2.$$

In I_1 put $u^2 = \dfrac{t+1}{b-t}$ so that $t = \dfrac{bu^2-1}{1+u^2}$,

$$dt = \frac{2(b+1)u\,du}{(1+u^2)^2},$$

$$a - t = \frac{a + 1 - (b-a)u^2}{1 + u^2}.$$

$$\therefore \quad I_1 = \int \frac{2(b+1)u^2 \, du}{(1+u^2)\{a+1-(b-a)u^2\}}$$

$$= \int \left\{ \frac{2(a+1)}{a+1-(b-a)u^2} - \frac{2}{1+u^2} \right\} du$$

$$= 2 \frac{a+1}{b-a} \int \frac{du}{\dfrac{a+1}{b-a} - u^2} - 2 \int \frac{du}{1+u^2}$$

$$= 2 \sqrt{\frac{a+1}{b-a}} \tanh^{-1} u \sqrt{\frac{b-a}{a+1}} - 2 \tan^{-1} u.$$

In I_2 put $v^2 = \dfrac{1-t}{b-t}$.

$$t = \frac{1 - bv^2}{1 - v^2}; \qquad dt = -\frac{2(b-1)v \, dv}{(1-v^2)^2}.$$

$$(a - t) = \frac{a - 1 + (b-a)v^2}{1 - v^2}.$$

$$\therefore \quad I_2 = -\int \frac{2(b-1)v^2 \, dv}{(1-v^2)\{a-1+(b-a)v^2\}}$$

$$= -2 \int \left\{ \frac{1}{1-v^2} - \frac{a-1}{a-1+(b-a)v^2} \right\} dv$$

$$= -2 \left\{ \tanh^{-1} v - \sqrt{\frac{a-1}{b-a}} \tan^{-1} v \sqrt{\frac{b-a}{a-1}} \right\}.$$

Hence

$$z = 2 \sqrt{\frac{a+1}{b-a}} \tanh^{-1} u \sqrt{\frac{b-a}{a+1}} - 2 \tan^{-1} u -$$

$$- 2j\lambda \left\{ \tanh^{-1} v - \sqrt{\frac{a-1}{b-a}} \tan^{-1} v \sqrt{\frac{b-a}{a-1}} \right\}. \qquad (5)$$

This result differs from the expression obtained by Cockcroft by employing the form $(1/c)\tanh^{-1}(u/c)$ instead of

$$\frac{1}{2c} \log \frac{c+u}{c-u},$$

and also by eliminating the constant of integration.

Mr. F. Bowman has shown that by taking the origin in the t-plane at O in Fig. 91, that is at the intersection of the lines EF

and AG, the constant of integration is eliminated. For at F, $t = -1$, $u = 0$, therefore z, as given by (5), is purely imaginary. Hence F is on the imaginary axis.

Also at G, $t = 1$, $v = 0$, therefore z, as given by (5), is real. Hence G is on the real axis. The intersection of the real and imaginary axes is the origin in the z-plane. Therefore the expression for z given in (5) requires no arbitrary constant.

The next step is to get expressions for the lengths of OG and OF in terms of a and b. Denote these two lengths by r_1 and r_2 respectively. In the case given below, where $g = h$, $r_1 = r_2 = r$, and if the curve between F and G were part of a circle, r would be the radius of that curve. For this reason r_1 and r_2 are nicknamed 'radii' although the curve FG is not a circle.

To find these lengths note that at G, $t = 1$, $z = r_1$, $v = 0$, $u = \sqrt{\dfrac{2}{b-1}}$. Filling in these values in (5),

$$\frac{r_1}{2} = \sqrt{\frac{a+1}{b-a}}\, \tanh^{-1} \sqrt{\left(\frac{2}{b-1}\right)\left(\frac{b-a}{a+1}\right)} - \tan^{-1}\sqrt{\frac{2}{b-1}}. \tag{6}$$

At F, $t = -1$, $z = r_2$, $u = 0$, $v = \sqrt{\dfrac{2}{b+1}}$.

$$\frac{r_2}{2} = \sqrt{\frac{(b+1)}{(b-1)}}\left\{ \tanh^{-1}\sqrt{\frac{2}{b+1}} - \sqrt{\frac{a-1}{b-a}}\, \tan^{-1}\sqrt{\left(\frac{2}{b+1}\right)\left(\frac{b-a}{a-1}\right)} \right\}. \tag{7}$$

To find the relation between h, g, a, and b, we know that at a long distance from the corner, say at the point A where $t = a$, the stress is ψ_1/h, and as ψ_1 has been taken as equal to π to simplify the formulae,

$$\frac{dw}{dz} = \frac{\pi}{h} = \frac{\sqrt{(b-a)}}{\sqrt{(a+1)} + \sqrt{\left(\frac{b+1}{b-1}\right)(a-1)}}.$$

This is derived from (3) by writing $\sqrt{(b-t)} = j\sqrt{(t-b)}$ and substituting a for t.

Hence,

$$h = \pi\left\{ \sqrt{\left(\frac{a+1}{b-a}\right)} + \sqrt{\left(\frac{b+1}{b-1}\right)\left(\frac{a-1}{b-a}\right)} \right\}. \tag{8}$$

By putting $t = \infty$ in (3) we get

$$g = \pi\left\{ 1 + \sqrt{\left(\frac{b+1}{b-1}\right)} \right\}. \tag{9}$$

In the case worked out by Cockcroft, where $h = g$, the expressions (8) and (9) must be equal. This is true when

$$\frac{b-a}{a-1} = \frac{b+1}{b-1} = \frac{a+1}{b-a}.$$

Applying these equalities to (6) and (7)

$$r_1 = r_2 = r = 2\sqrt{\left(\frac{b+1}{b-1}\right)}\tanh^{-1}\sqrt{\frac{2}{b+1}} - 2\tan^{-1}\sqrt{\frac{2}{b-1}}. \quad (10)$$

We will call the electric stress in the gap at a distance from the corner, 'the mean stress'. This is ψ_1/g; and since ψ_1 is taken as π, we have from (9),

$$\text{mean stress} = \frac{1}{1+\sqrt{\left(\frac{b+1}{b-1}\right)}}.$$

We have seen (p. 110) that the stress over the curve is $\sqrt{\dfrac{b-1}{2}}$.

Therefore the ratio

$$\frac{\text{stress over curve}}{\text{mean stress}} = \frac{\sqrt{(b+1)}+\sqrt{(b-1)}}{\sqrt{2}}.$$

Thus we have r, g, and the stress ratio in terms of b, and it is possible to plot a curve showing how the stress ratio changes with the ratio r/g. This Cockcroft has done. With this introduction the reader will have no difficulty in completing this example from Cockcroft's paper.

INDEX